Fiction in Action
Whodunit

Adam Gray
Marcos Benevides

Acknowledgements

The authors would like to acknowledge our Kansai Gaidai University students without whom this project would not have been possible. Thank you also to KGU Intensive English Studies Department Director Dr. Francis Lindsey, and faculty members Ellen McFarland, Lisa Peoria, John Stark, and Derek Weygandt, and all of your students.

"For Roberto and Marilda; and for Katty, the real Ellie Koo."

Writers: Adam Gray and Marcos Benevides
Editor: Hugh Graham-Marr
Cover Design: Design Office Terra, Tokyo
Layout: Christopher Hanzie Design, Tokyo/Singapore
Illustrations: Yuji Tachikawa

ABAX Ltd. Tokyo and San Francisco
www.abax.net

Printed in Singapore

Introduction

In this class, you will read two original detective stories. Each story is divided into six chapters. At the beginning of each chapter, there is a pre-reading section (for example, page 8). Answer these questions before reading the chapter.

While you read the chapter, look for fingerprint clues like this one: ; you may find some important information nearby. You will also find some interactive illustrations to help you understand the story better (for example, *The Reed's Bedroom* on page 12). Near the end of each chapter there is a puzzle which is part of that chapter (for example, page 15 with questions on pages 16 and 17).

Read each chapter and complete the puzzle by yourself for homework. At the end of each chapter there is a review section (for example, pages 18 and 19). These are in-class group discussion activities. Use this class time to check your understanding of the story, to talk about reading strategies, and to ask language questions of your group members or your teacher.

But most important of all, please enjoy reading the stories!

Sincerely,
Adam Gray and Marcos Benevides

Contents

Planning Your Reading

A. What are your reading habits?

How well do each of the statements below describe your current reading habits? Remember, even good readers have different reading habits, so there are no right or wrong answers. The purpose of this exercise is just to make you think about how, where and when you read, so that you can best plan your future reading schedule.

	No ← → Yes			
1. I like to read for fun in my native language.	1	2	3	4
2. It is possible to enjoy reading and to learn something new at the same time.	1	2	3	4
3. I spend several hours each week reading in my native language.	1	2	3	4
4. I want to read more, but I just don't have the time lately.	1	2	3	4
5. My reading skills in my native language help me to read in English.	1	2	3	4
6. I enjoy reading in English.	1	2	3	4
7. I read a variety of things; for example, stories, newspapers, etc.	1	2	3	4
8. I only read for specific purposes; for example, for a class or for work.	1	2	3	4
9. I can read anywhere; for example, on a bus, in a noisy restaurant, etc.	1	2	3	4
10. I can read anytime; for example, late at night, on a short break, etc.	1	2	3	4
11. I often stop to check the dictionary or the Internet while I am reading.	1	2	3	4
12. Before reading a book, it is important to think about its cover, the title, and the summary on the back cover.	1	2	3	4
13. I like to take notes while I read.	1	2	3	4
14. When I become confused about the facts in a story, I always stop and go back to find out where I went wrong.	1	2	3	4
15. I've stayed up too late at night, missed my bus stop, or forgot an important appointment because I couldn't stop reading.	1	2	3	4

B. What are your reading habits?

1. From the table in Part A, choose three or four statements about your reading habits which are most important for you. They can be positive or negative statements. Write them below.

Example: *I can't read in noisy places.*

_____

_____

_____

_____

2. Now, discuss your reading habits with a partner. Suggest ways that you can plan or improve your reading experience. Remember that everyone has different reading preferences.

C. Make your ideal reading plan.

Use the space below to describe your ideal reading plan. You can make a weekly schedule, describe your plan in a few short sentences, or make a drawing. The important thing is to think about *how*, *when* and *where* you will be reading over the next few weeks so that you can both enjoy the experience and continue to develop your best reading habits.

_____

_____

_____

_____

_____

_____

_____

_____

_____

_____

_____

_____

_____

_____

_____

Story 1
The Inverted Eagle
by Adam Gray

Crime Talk

The following words and expressions will be important for understanding and talking about this story. Look for a list of Crime Talk words at the beginning of each chapter (for example, page 9). Those are the Crime Talk words that will appear in that chapter.

accuse – say that someone did a crime

alibi – proof that you were elsewhere at the time of a crime and so could not do the crime

attorney – a lawyer

behind bars – in jail

case – a police investigation

clue – an item or piece of information that helps solve a case

fingerprints – marks left by fingers (everybody has different fingerprints)

frame – use false evidence to make an innocent person seem guilty of a crime

motive – a reason to commit a crime

proof or **evidence*** – facts or objects that show who probably did a crime

robbery – a theft; the stealing of something using force

under arrest – taken by the police; charged with a crime

victim – a person who is hurt or killed in a crime or accident

* Note: **Proof** and **evidence** are uncountable nouns.
You can say:
   • "Does he have *some* proof?" or "She found *three pieces of* evidence."
But you cannot say:
   • "She has ~~three proofs~~." or "He found ~~many evidences~~."

What word or expression is shown by each picture? Write it in the space.

_____   _____   _____

Chapter 1: Pre-reading

In this chapter, we meet Detective Eliana "Ellie" Koo, the hero of the story. She works for the Washington DC Police Department. She must investigate a crime in a very rich neighborhood of the city.

• **Answer these pre-reading questions alone or with a partner. If you don't know the answer, guess.**

1. What does "whodunit" mean? Hint: It's three words mashed together.

   _____

2. What is the job of a police detective? How is it different from a police officer?

   _____

3. What do you think "the scene of the crime" means?

   _____

4. Have you read any interesting crime stories before, or watched them on TV? What usually happens in these stories?

   _____

   _____

   _____

Chapter 1

Crime Talk: case, fingerprint, robbery, victim

The Scene of the Crime

Detective Eliana Koo stepped out of her car and stared at the front of the huge house at 329   1
Birch Drive. She couldn't believe that anyone would want to live in such an enormous house. It was
bigger than her entire apartment building in the Mount Pleasant neighborhood of Washington, DC.

"Ellie," called a familiar voice. "Over here."

Ellie looked from door to window to window, but couldn't see anyone. "Where?"   5

"Look up."

In a third floor window she spotted the gray hair of her friend Officer Kazuo Yokota, a veteran
Washington DC police officer. Fifteen years earlier, when Ellie became a police officer, Yokota helped
and supported her like an older brother. They were still close friends.

"I'll be up in a minute," she shouted. "If I don't get lost."   10

A young officer opened the front door and showed Ellie where the stairs were. Soon she was
face to face with Yokota. His police uniform fit a little more tightly than before, but his face was still
thin and handsome.

"Well, what happened?" she asked, shaking her friend's hand.

"A drugging, a robbery, and almost a murder."   15

"*Almost* is an important word," Ellie said, smiling. She took out her detective's notebook and a pen from inside her long black coat. "Details?"

Yokota took out his own notebook. "This home belongs to Evan and Nancy Reed, ages fifty-two and fifty. Mr. Reed is an executive with Washington Bank. Mrs. Reed is a retired lawyer. This morning, at about 9:00, the housekeeper found them unconscious in their bedroom and called 9-1-1. Their wall safe, located above their bed, was open and empty. Nancy Reed was barely breathing and almost died, but both victims are doing well now. The doctors expect them both to recover. We aren't sure yet, but it looks like someone put some pills in their evening tea."

"What was stolen from the safe?"

"According to Judith Reed, who is Evan's mother, there was a box of Nancy Reed's jewelry inside the safe. The jewelry was worth more than $400,000. There was also cash, about $80,000. Finally, there was a collection of rare stamps that belonged to Judith Reed. They were worth about $40,000. She bought her most valuable stamp, an 'Inverted Eagle' stamp, less than a week ago."

Ellie nodded as she wrote her notes. Her nickname, Ellie, was short for Eliana, but it was also short for Elephant. She earned this nickname as a police officer because she never forgot any details about a case, just like in the proverb 'an elephant never forgets.' Ellie, however, did not have a better memory than most other detectives. Her secret was that she took detailed notes and studied them frequently.

"Who else lives in the house?" she asked.

"Five other people live here. I already mentioned Judith Reed. She has lived here with her son and daughter-in-law for three years, since her husband died. The Reeds have two children who also live here. Kevin Reed is twenty-four years old. He's unemployed and lives here all year. Allison Reed is twenty-one. She's a student at Brown University, and only lives here during the summer. She was planning on leaving Washington in less than a week to return to college. By the way, she is engaged to marry Derrick Quenton, the son of Ted Quenton."

"Ted Quenton? The owner of Quenton Hotels?"

Yokota nodded. "Ted Quenton is one of the richest people in the country."

"Rich people shouldn't be allowed to marry other rich people," Ellie joked.

"I agree," said Yokota, smiling. "One of them should marry me! Anyway, the other two people who live here are Lucia Deza, the housekeeper, and her son, Miguel. Lucia was born in Peru, like you, but has lived in the U.S. for almost fifteen years. Miguel is nineteen years old, and a pre-med student at Georgetown University."

"Georgetown?" asked Ellie, very surprised. "Georgetown is a very expensive university. How can the son of a housekeeper afford to go there?"

The Families: Complete this chart of members of the Reed and Deza families. Write in the missing names.

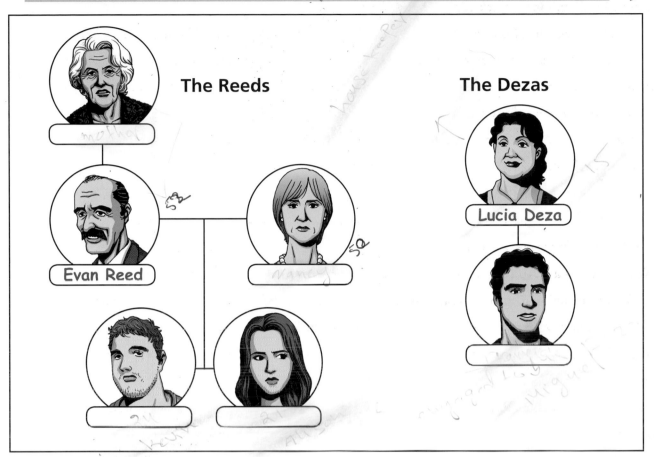

The Reeds

The Dezas

mother

Evan Reed

Nancy

Lucia Deza

Kevin 24

Allison 21

grandson Miguel

"Miguel is smart. He earned a full scholarship, so the university pays for his education. He keeps   50
the scholarship by getting very high grades."

"Good for him," Ellie said. She knew first-hand how challenging it could be for a child of
immigrants to find success in the U.S. Her own parents brought her to the U.S. from Peru when she was
eight. Even now, thirty years later, she remembered the first few difficult years very clearly.

"Judith, Kevin, and Allison Reed just came back from the hospital. Do you want to interview   55
them?"

"In a minute," Ellie said, scribbling in her notebook. "I want to look at the bedroom first."

Yokota led Ellie down a long hallway. The Reeds' bedroom door was open. Ellie noticed a set of
keys still hanging from the keyhole. Inside, several police officers were dusting for fingerprints.

"Who found the Reeds this morning?" she asked, inspecting the keys.   60

Yokota returned to his notebook. "Let's see. Mr. Reed's mother, Judith, knocked on the door
this morning at about 8:50. She was worried because the Reeds usually wake up around 7:30. No one
answered, so she went to find Lucia, the housekeeper. Together they opened the door around 9:00."

"Could you bring Judith and Lucia here?"

Yokota nodded and left Ellie alone in the doorway. Inside the bedroom she was greeted by   65
another officer who was taking photographs.

"Has anything been moved?" Ellie asked.

"No, ma'am," said the young officer. "This is exactly how the room looked when we arrived."

Ellie ran her fingers through her straight, black hair, studying the scene. The first thing she
noticed was the huge bed directly in front of her. On the right side of the bed, near the pillow, was   70
an open book, an empty teacup, and a set of reading glasses. Next to this side of the bed was a small
table that held a lamp, a pile of papers, a coaster with the same design as the teacup, a wallet, and an
expensive-looking watch. The lamp was on. On the left side of the bed there was nothing unusual, but
on the floor was a spilled teacup. Next to the teacup was a large wet spot.

"That wet spot, is that tea?" Ellie asked the officer.   75

"Yes, ma'am," answered the officer, putting down her camera. "We've sent a sample to the crime
lab to see if it was drugged."

Next to the left side of the bed was another table. It held another lamp, though this one was
turned off. Another set of reading glasses were resting upon a closed book, which was next to an alarm
clock. There was also another coaster.   80

Above the bed was a large still-life painting of some yellow flowers, but Ellie's eyes focused
behind the painting. The painting swung open from the left, revealing a hidden wall safe. The safe was
open, and completely empty.

The Reeds' Bedroom: Use Ellie's description to draw in objects and complete the picture of the scene. Pay attention to details.

Ellie put on a pair of gloves and walked to the right side of the bed. The watch was a Rolex, probably worth around $3,000. Inside the wallet she found Evan Reed's driver's license, his credit cards, and $45 in cash. Why didn't the thief steal these items?

Ellie heard the sound of footsteps behind her. She turned to find Yokota standing in the doorway. He stepped inside, followed by Judith Reed. Ms. Reed was seventy-seven years old, but at the moment looked a lot older. Her narrow face was very pale, and her eyes were wet with tears. She walked very slowly, with the help of a cane. Ellie immediately felt sorry for the woman, who reminded her of her own grandmother back in Peru. Behind her, Lucia Deza looked down at her feet, hesitated for a moment, and then followed Ms. Reed into the room. She looked just as tired. The housekeeper glanced nervously around the room, but didn't look Ellie in the eye.

"I'm Detective Koo," Ellie said, smiling at the two women. "I'm in charge of the investigation." She took off her gloves, put them in her coat pockets, and shook the hands of both women.

Judith Reed introduced herself. Then it was Lucia's turn. Lucia spoke English very well, so Ellie decided not to tell her that she was also Peruvian. Ellie's father was the son of Chinese immigrants to Peru, so Ellie did not look like a typical Peruvian. Most people who met her thought she was from Indonesia or the Philippines.

Ellie wasn't very tall, at 5'3", and was one of only a few female detectives on the police force. However, she never had any problem commanding the respect of fellow officers or people involved in a case. Her strong voice, straight posture, direct eye contact, and professional appearance were signs of her confidence which people usually noticed. Her large, almond-shaped eyes could be very warm, but they could also be cold and serious when she wanted them to be. Now, they were friendly.

"Ms. Reed, can you please tell me what happened this morning?" Ellie asked gently.

"You see, my son always wakes up early. This morning I didn't see him in the kitchen. I always see him in the kitchen, you see. He drinks a cup of coffee and reads the newspaper. I waited and then decided to knock on the door. No one answered, so I looked all over the house for Lucia. I couldn't find her anywhere, then finally saw her outside in the garden. I went outside, brought her in, and we knocked again. Then she opened the door, and we saw..." Judith started crying, and Yokota offered her a tissue.

"Ms. Deza, what did you see?" Ellie asked.

"It was terrible," whispered the housekeeper. "I thought they were... gone. Mr. Reed was there." She pointed to the right side of the bed. "His book was on his chest. His head was against the headboard. His teacup was upside-down on the bed. And Mrs. Reed, *pobrecita*, she was lying down, her hands folded on her stomach, holding her teacup. She looked like an angel. We called out their names, but they didn't move. I shook Mrs. Reed, and the cup slipped from her hand and the tea spilled all over the floor. Still she did not wake up. That's when I called 9-1-1."

Ellie had her notebook out again. "Ms. Reed," she asked, "is that how you remember it?"

"Yes," answered the old woman, still crying but not as hard. 120

"Ms. Deza, did you bring them the tea last night?"

Lucia looked away from Ellie, and Ellie noticed that her hands were shaking. "Yes, I always bring them tea before bed."

"What time was that?"

"9:30, like always. I knocked on the door and Mrs. Reed told me to come in. I unlocked the 125 door, gave Mrs. Reed her tea, and put Mr. Reed's tea on the table near the bed. Then I left and locked the door."

"Where was Mr. Reed?"

"I heard the shower. He always takes a shower at night."

Ellie looked up from her notebook and smiled at Lucia, trying to calm her. "You prepared the tea 130 in the kitchen?"

"Yes," she answered, quickly.

"Alone?"

The housekeeper looked down to the floor and nodded.

"Did you leave the kitchen for any reason? Could someone else have drugged the tea?" 135

"I don't remember," whispered Lucia. "I might have gone to the bathroom, or sometimes I sit in the dining room while the water is boiling. I'm sorry, I don't know."

Ellie smiled, but wasn't sure she believed the housekeeper. Lucia was hiding something. "And after preparing the tea? What did you do then?"

"I went to sleep. My room is next to my son's, on the first floor." 140

Ellie turned to Judith. "Ms. Reed, who knows the combination to the wall safe?"

"Only Evan, Nancy, and I."

"Only the three of you?"

"That's what I said," answered the old woman, with a little anger in her voice. Ellie noticed that she had stopped crying. 145

"Well, whoever opened the safe knew the combination, because it wasn't forced open," Ellie said politely. "And the bedroom here. Is it always locked?"

"Always," answered Lucia. "Mr. and Mrs. Reed insist that their bedroom door must always be locked."

"And the key to the bedroom? Who has a key?"

"There are four keys," answered Ms. Reed, calmly now. "Evan has one, Nancy has one, Lucia has one, and I have one."

Ellie stopped writing and looked up, confused. "Ms. Reed, if you have a key, why did you look for Lucia this morning? Why didn't you open the door yourself?"

Her cheeks blushing, Judith Reed answered…

155

" I		h	a		e	n	' t		s	e	e	n		m	y		k	e	y	s
5		8	18	16	13	6	10		20	2	13	6		9	19		1	17	19	20

?	i		t	w	o		d	a	y	s	.	I		t	h	i	n	k
5	6		12	3	7		11	18	19	4		5		12	8	5	6	1

					e		s	t	o	l	e				e		. "
4	15	9	2	7	6	13		20	10	15	14	2		12	8	17	9

"Did you tell this to anyone?" Ellie asked.

"No," muttered Judith. "I was too embarrassed. Besides, I thought I would find them eventually. But I've looked everywhere."

Ellie nodded and turned to Yokota. "I think it's time to meet the others."

END OF CHAPTER 1

Instructions:

To discover what Judith Reed said, answer the following vocabulary and comprehension questions. After you have answered all of the questions, use the letters of the correct responses and the circled letters to solve the puzzle on page 15.

Example:

1) The opposite of <u>older</u> is:
   (a) younger   b) prettier   c) friendlier   d) smaller

2) In what country was Ellie born?
   (P) E R U

Example Puzzle:
Ellie calls her father P A P A .
                        2 1 2 1

A. Vocabulary Questions

1) "Fifteen years earlier, when Ellie became a police officer, Yokota helped and supported her like an older brother." (Line 9) All of the following expressions show <u>support</u> for someone *except*:
   j) "You can do it!"
   k) "Sorry, but I'm too busy."
   l) "What can I do to help you?"
   m) "You're doing an excellent job."

2) "Soon she was face to face with Yokota." (Line 12) Which of the following conversations is <u>face to face</u>?
   e) talking in a coffee shop
   f) sending instant messages on-line
   g) talking over the phone
   h) texting on a cell phone

3) "This morning, at about 9:00, the housekeeper found them unconscious in their bedroom and called 9-1-1." (Line 20)

   If you are <u>unconscious</u>, you are not

   A(w) a r e .

4) "Their wall safe, located above their bed, was open and empty."(Line 21) Which of the following items would you perhaps find in a <u>safe</u>?
   r) shoe polish
   s) diamonds
   t) makeup
   u) medicine

5) "Finally, there was a collection of rare stamps that belonged to Judith Reed." (Line 27) Usually, <u>stamps</u> are attached to pieces of:
   h) food
   i) mail
   j) clothing
   k) furniture

6) "Ellie nodded as she wrote her notes." (Line 29) To <u>nod</u> means to move your head:
   m) in a circle
   n) up and down
   o) side to side
   p) backwards

   Why do people usually nod?

   to show they agreed

7) "Kevin Reed is twenty-four years old. He is unemployed and lives here all year." (Line 37)

   If you are <u>unemployed</u>, then you don't have a

   J (o) b .

8) "Miguel is nineteen years old, and a pre-med student at Georgetown University." (Line 46) <u>Pre</u> means before, and <u>med</u> is short for medicine. So, Miguel is studying to become a(n):
   g) lawyer
   h) doctor
   i) actor
   j) politician

9) "We've sent a sample [of the tea] to the crime lab to see if it was drugged." (Line 76) If a substance, like tea, is <u>drugged</u>, then:
   k) the substance is completely safe
   l) someone checked to see if it had drugs in it
   m) someone put a drug in it
   n) someone took a drug out of it

10) "Behind her, Lucia Deza looked down at her feet, hesitated for a moment, and then followed Ms. Reed into the room." (Line 91) It is common to <u>hesitate</u> in all of the following situations *except*:
- q) you don't remember which way to go
- r) you are nervous in front of a powerful person
- s) you are not sure what to say
- (t) you hear a fire alarm

What does it mean to hesitate?

it means a person doesn't know to do something because one is not sure it is right.

11) "I'm Detective Koo. I'm in charge of the investigation." (Line 94)

The person who is <u>in charge of</u> a group or an activity is the L _e_ _a_ (_d_)E R of that group or activity.

12) "Ms. Reed, who knows the combination to the wall safe?" (Line 141) A <u>combination</u> is a(n):
- (t) series of numbers used to open a lock
- u) cover used to hide a safe
- v) special key for opening a safe
- w) identification card

B. Comprehension Questions

13) Which item was *not* stolen from the Reeds' safe?
- d) a jewelry box
- e) an expensive watch
- f) cash
- g) a collection of rare stamps

14) How did the thief *probably* knock the Reeds unconscious?
- j) by drugging their food
- k) by hitting them on the head
- (l) by drugging their tea
- m) by drugging their clothing

15) Ellie is impressed because Miguel earned a full scholarship to attend Georgetown University. How does Miguel keep the scholarship?
- l) by playing sports
- m) by working in the library
- n) by helping other students learn Spanish
- (o) by getting good grades

16) Ellie noticed all of the following objects on Evan Reed's table *except*:
- s) an expensive watch
- t) a wallet
- u) a lamp
- (v) a book

17) What can we guess about Ellie?
- d) She would like to own a big house.
- (e) She speaks at least two languages.
- f) She is not respected by other police officers.
- g) She joined the police when she was thirty years old.

18) Why is Lucia *probably* nervous?
- (a) She prepared the tea.
- b) She disliked the Reeds.
- c) She lost her keys.
- d) She and Ellie are both from Peru.

19) Who does *not* know the combination to the wall safe?
- v) Evan
- w) Judith
- x) Nancy
- (y) Lucia

20) How much time passed between Lucia giving the Reeds their evening tea, and Judith and Lucia finding them the next morning?
- q) eight and a half hours
- r) nine and a half hours
- (s) eleven and a half hours
- t) twelve and a half hours

Now, go back to page 15 and fill in the puzzle answers to find out what Judith said.

A. Police Briefing

Get into small groups and select a chief detective. The chief detective will lead group discussions, and make sure all members are participating.

1. Check your Chapter 1 puzzle answers with your group.

2. Discuss the evidence and complete the box below.

> What is the sequence of important events from the time Lucia brings the tea to the Reeds in the evening, until she calls 9-1-1 the next morning?

Time (If Known)	What Happens?
9:30 p.m.	Lucia brings tea to Nancy and Evan Reed, as usual.

B. **Listen to the CD**

You will hear the call to 9-1-1 made by Lucia, the housekeeper. After you listen, answer the questions.

1. How does Lucia sound on the phone? Circle as many as necessary:

> nervous   worried   happy   calm   guilty   innocent
>
> drugged   sleepy   confused   honest   angry   panicked

2. Why does Lucia put down the phone in the middle of the conversation?

_____

3. Does anything about the call make you suspicious? Why? Discuss.

_____

C. Think Ahead

Which of the following scenarios is probably true? Discuss your reasons.

☐ This is a home robbery. The criminal is probably a stranger to the family.

☐ This is a home robbery. The criminal is probably a family member.

☐ This is an attempted murder. The criminal is probably a stranger.

☐ This is an attempted murder. The criminal is probably an acquaintance.

☐ Another possibility: _____

D. Quiz

Complete the quiz. You may use your Detective's Notebook, but close this book.

Previously in *Whodunit... The Scene of the Crime*

The following panels show three important events from Chapter 1. Order and caption each panel. The first one has been done for you.

Lucia found the Reeds unconscious.

Chapter 2 : Three Interviews

In this chapter, Ellie interviews three suspects in the case. Kevin and Allison are the son and daughter of the victims, and Miguel is the son of their housekeeper. All three live in the house.

• **Answer these pre-reading questions alone or with a partner. If you don't know the answer, guess.**

1. What are three questions that a police detective might ask a suspect?

   Q1: _____

   Q2: _____

   Q3: _____

2. List one key fact about each character:

   Lucia Deza: _____   Evan Reed: _____

   Miguel Deza: _____   Kevin Reed: _____

   Judith Reed: _____   Allison Reed: _____

   Nancy Reed: _____   Kazuo Yokota: _____

3. In Chapter 2, Ellie discovers that Judith Reed lied to her. What do you think she lied about?

   _____

Chapter 2

Three Interviews

Kevin   Miguel   Allison

Ellie chose the most comfortable chair in the Reeds' library and sat down. Even in the warm library she did not take off her long, black coat. Some friends joked that she even slept in her coat. From the library, she could see police officers down the hall going in and out of the Reeds' bedroom. The library itself was a small but charming room. It was full of wooden bookshelves which held dozens of books, several picture frames, and countless little knick-knacks that Ellie's mother would have called *basura*. Ellie smiled as she pictured her parents' simple house. The only decorations that Ellie's mother put on the wall were pictures of her grandchildren, including Ellie's twelve-year-old daughter, Sofia.

Ellie's cell phone rang. It was a doctor at the crime lab. He confirmed that the Reeds' tea had been drugged with sleeping pills. He told Ellie the name of the drug and said that they were very powerful pills that you could only get with a prescription. Nancy Reed was allergic to these sleeping pills, which was why she almost stopped breathing, and why she almost died.

Seconds after Ellie hung up, Yokota entered the library with Kevin Reed. Kevin was wearing old blue jeans, a dirty green T-shirt, and socks with holes in them. He was a little overweight, and looked like he hadn't shaved in about four days. He yawned as Ellie invited him to sit down across from her.

1

5

10

15

"You must be Kevin," Ellie began. "I'm Detective Koo. I'm in charge of the investigation."

"I don't know why you want to talk with me first," Kevin said aggressively. "Did somebody accuse me of something? I didn't do anything wrong."

"Then you have nothing to worry about," Ellie said calmly. "Kevin, does anyone in the house have a prescription for sleeping pills?" 20

"Sleeping pills? Yeah, my dad takes them. They're probably in his bathroom."

Ellie nodded at Yokota, who disappeared. Then she opened her notebook. "All right, Kevin. Tell me where you were and what you did last night."

"I went to an afternoon movie with some friends, but I got home at around 7:00. I ate dinner with my family until about 7:30, then I went to my room to play video games. I went to sleep at about 25 midnight."

"Midnight? That's a lot of video games!"

"I like video games," Kevin said, loudly. "Is that a crime?"

"No, I don't think so," Ellie said, though in her home it was a crime—Sofia could only play video games for twenty minutes a night. "Where is your bedroom?" 30

"Downstairs, on the second floor."

"And did you hear any strange noises last night?"

"No, nothing. I woke up this morning when I heard my grandma screaming."

Ellie nodded and wrote. "I was told that you are unemployed right now?"

Kevin sighed and looked around the library. "Is that a crime, too?" 35

Ellie smiled. "What is your financial situation?"

"My financial situation is none of your business," growled Kevin.

"I'm afraid it is my business," answered Ellie. "The thief stole a lot of money."

"My parents take care of me. They give me an allowance of $200 a week, so I have no reason to steal their money." 40

Ellie smiled a tiny smile. She could not imagine giving Sofia $200 a week to play video games and go to movies.

"Kevin, do you have a key to your parents' bedroom?"

"No."

"Have you seen your grandmother's keys?" 45

"Why, did she lose them?" Kevin asked, laughing.

"The combination to the wall safe," Ellie said quickly, looking Kevin in the eye. "Do you know it?"

"Are you kidding? Do you think they trust me with the combination to the safe? They'd never tell me."

"All right," Ellie said, thinking that she wouldn't trust Kevin with the combination either. "If I have any further questions, I will call you back in."

Kevin left the library. Ellie didn't particularly like Kevin, but agreed that he had little reason to steal the contents of the safe. In addition, the person who opened the safe knew the combination, and Kevin didn't know it.

Yokota entered the library and showed her a bottle of pills.

"In the bathroom?" she asked.

He nodded. "It's about half empty."

"Call the crime lab, please, and tell them what you found. I'm ready for the sister in here."

Allison Reed was completely unlike her brother. Her brown hair was long and well-styled, and her black blouse and khaki pants were clean and fashionable. She was also very pretty, with the same brown eyes as her grandmother.

"I'll help you any way I can," she said to Ellie after their introductions. "I can't believe anyone would do this to my parents."

"Let's start with your whereabouts last night."

"I have a summer job at the library. After work, at about 7:00, I came home and had dinner with my family. We finished around 7:30. Then I talked with my father here, in the library, until about 8:30. Then he said he was going to his bedroom, so I went to the basement and watched a movie until about 10:30. I was tired after the movie, so I went to bed."

"You didn't call your fiancé?" Ellie asked quickly.

"Derrick?" she asked, surprised by the question. "No, I didn't call him. We talked a few days ago."

"And your job? Which library?"

Allison again looked surprised, and hesitated before answering, "At the university."

"Which university?"

"Georgetown, just a few blocks from here. I work in the Psychology Library."

Allison seemed nervous about something. Ellie decided to change the subject. "What did you and your father talk about?"

Allison shrugged. "I don't know, the usual. He asked me about college, and if I was excited to go back."

"Are you excited to go back?"

"I guess. Now I don't know what to do, with my parents in the hospital."

"What else did you talk about?"

"Let's see. My father wanted my opinion about a building project he has. He and some partners are building some condominiums in Springfield, Virginia."

Ellie was confused. Allison studied psychology at Brown University, not engineering or architecture. "What did he ask you?"

"Oh, he was wondering if Derrick's father, Ted Quenton, might want to invest some money, to become a partner in the project."

"What did you tell him?"

"I said probably not, since Mr. Quenton owns hotels, not condos. I also told him that I didn't feel comfortable asking Mr. Quenton about it, and my father understood."

Ellie then asked Allison about the keys to the bedroom and the combination to the safe. Allison confirmed what the others had said—that only Evan, Nancy, Judith, and Lucia had keys to the bedroom, and that only Evan, Nancy, and Judith knew the combination to the safe. She told Ellie that her bedroom was on the second floor, near her brother's, and that she did not hear or notice anything unusual during the night.

"Allison," Ellie finally asked, "can you think of anyone who would do this to your parents?"

"I've been thinking and thinking, but I really can't think of anyone. I have no idea who drugged them and opened the safe."

Ellie asked quietly, "Could it have been your brother?"

"No way!" Allison exclaimed. "He's lazy, but he would never do this."

"And Miguel?"

Allison's expression became very serious. "Just because he isn't rich doesn't mean that he is a thief! Miguel is a wonderful person. He would never, never hurt anyone."

Ellie smiled and said, "I'm not rich, and I am not a thief, so you don't need to explain the world to me. Miguel lives in this house, and there is no sign that anyone broke into the house, so he is a suspect."

"Talk to him and you'll see," Allison said passionately. "He's innocent."

Ellie thanked Allison and asked to see Miguel. Allison Reed seemed like the perfect daughter, but there was something about her that Ellie didn't trust. She suspected that the perfect daughter might be hiding a secret or two.

Miguel entered wearing a Georgetown T-shirt and black sweatpants. He ran his fingers through his short hair, took a deep breath, and sat down across from Ellie. Like his mother, Miguel seemed anxious.

"It looks like you're sweating, Mr. Deza," Ellie said quickly.

85

90

95

100

105

110

115

"It's hot in here," Miguel answered just as quickly. He eyed Ellie's coat. "Aren't you hot?"

"You look afraid," Ellie said, ignoring his question. "Are you?"

"I have something to tell you that will make me look guilty, but I swear to you that I didn't harm 120
the Reeds," Miguel said. The young man had an honest face, but Ellie had seen many lies come out of
honest faces in the past.

"What do you want to say?" she asked.

Miguel took another deep breath and said, "Last week, the Reeds asked me to move out of their
house by the end of the month. I have been looking for apartments, but everything in the Georgetown 125
area is very expensive. My mother said she would help me, but she doesn't have much money, either. I
don't know where I'm going to live."

"Did they give you a reason? Why do they want you to move out now?"

"I don't know. Mrs. Reed didn't give me a reason. She just said that it was time for me to find my
own place." 130

Ellie looked up from her notebook. "Were you angry?"

"No," Miguel said quickly. Then he half-smiled and added, "Well, maybe a little angry. But
really, I was just surprised, and hurt. I've lived here since the Reeds hired my mom, six years ago. I sleep
in an extra bedroom that the Reeds don't need, and I help them out whenever I can. I thought we had a
nice relationship, so I don't know why they want me to leave." 135

Ellie wondered what had happened last week to make the Reeds change their minds about
Miguel. "So it was Mrs. Reed who told you to move out, not Mr. Reed?"

"Mrs. Reed told me, but she said that Mr. Reed agreed."

"And what does your mother say about this?"

Quietly and sadly, Miguel said, "She isn't happy, but she can't say anything to the Reeds. She 140
doesn't want to lose her job."

"And Kevin and Allison? What do they think about you moving out?"

Miguel became very still. "I don't think they know. I didn't tell either of them."

Ellie felt sorry for Miguel, but also knew that he had a strong motive for stealing the contents of
the safe—he needed money, and had reason to be angry. 145

"Where were you and what did you do last night?"

"I'm taking summer classes at the university, and I came home after my last class at about 7:15.
My mother had just finished making dinner for the Reeds, so she and I ate in the kitchen for about
fifteen minutes. Then I helped her with the laundry for a half hour, watched a little TV in the basement,
and went to my room to read my biology homework." 150

"And what time was that?"

"I don't know. About 8:30, I guess. I studied until 11:00 and went to sleep."

Ellie looked through her notebook quickly. The tea was probably drugged at about 9:25 p.m., and all five residents—Judith, Lucia, Kevin, Allison, and Miguel—were alone at that time. No alibis.

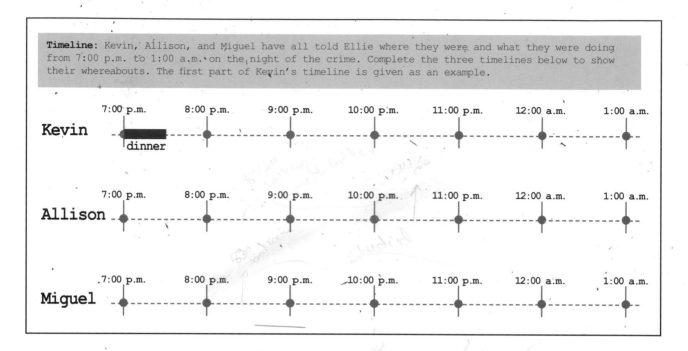

Timeline: Kevin, Allison, and Miguel have all told Ellie where they were and what they were doing from 7:00 p.m. to 1:00 a.m. on the night of the crime. Complete the three timelines below to show their whereabouts. The first part of Kevin's timeline is given as an example.

"Miguel, you are studying medicine?"

Miguel nodded. "I just finished my first year at Georgetown."

"The thief used Mr. Reed's sleeping pills to drug the Reeds. Unfortunately, Mrs. Reed was allergic to the pills, and she almost died." Ellie gave Miguel her most serious look. "You study medicine, Miguel. The thief used medicine to drug the Reeds. What do you think about that?"

"Listen, everyone in the house knows about Mr. Reed's sleeping pills. He complains about them all the time. It doesn't take special medical knowledge to crush some pills and put them in tea."

"How did you know the pills were crushed in the tea? I didn't tell you that."

Miguel frowned, and said quietly, "My mother told me, before I came in here."

Ellie nodded and made more notes in the notebook. Finally she asked, "Everyone has told me that only Evan, Nancy, and Judith Reed knew the combination to the safe. Is this true?"

Miguel took his deepest breath yet, and said, "It's better if I tell you the truth now. The truth is . . .

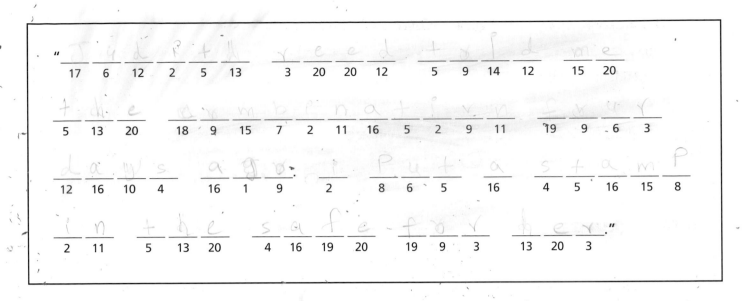

```
"  J    u    d    i    t    h        r    e    e    d         t    o    l    d         m    e
   17   6    12   2    5    13       3    20   20   12        5    9    14   12        15   20

   t    h    e         c    o    m    b    i    n    a    t    i    o    n         f    o    u    r
   5    13   20        18   9    15   7    2    11   16   5    2    9    11        19   9    6    3

   d    a    y    s         a    g    o    .    i        P    u    t         a         s    t    a    m    P
   12   16   10   4         16   1    9    2    8    6    5         16        4    5    16   15   8

   i    n         t    h    e         s    a    f    e         f    o    r         h    e    r    ."
   2    11        5    13   20        4    16   19   20        19   9    3         13   20   3
```

Ellie closed her eyes, hiding her anger. She didn't like it when people lied to her.

"Are you sure it was four days ago?"

"Yes," Miguel said. "I remember because it was Sunday and no one else was home."

"And that was the only time you opened the safe?"

Miguel nodded, and laughed. "Bad luck, right?"

Ellie didn't believe in luck, good or bad. She thanked Miguel for his time and yelled to Yokota,

"I want to see Judith Reed *right now*."

175

Instructions:

To discover what Miguel said, answer the following vocabulary and comprehension questions. After you have answered all of the questions, use the letters of the correct responses and the circled letters to solve the puzzle on page 27.

A. Vocabulary Questions

1) "It was full of wooden bookshelves which held dozens of books, several picture frames, and countless little knick-knacks that Ellie's mother would have called *basura*." (Line 5)
Knick-knacks are usually _____ objects that are kept for _____
- g) small; decoration
- h) expensive; emergencies
- i) large; education
- (j) important; holidays

2) "He confirmed that the Reeds' tea had been drugged with sleeping pills." (Line 9)
A <u>pill</u> is a small tablet or piece of

M e d (i) c i n e

3) "He told Ellie the name of the drug and said that they were very powerful pills that you could only get with a prescription." (Line 10) A <u>prescription</u> is:
- (r) an order for medicine that a doctor gives
- s) a liquid that helps you sleep
- t) a strong interest in something
- u) an allergy

4) "Nancy Reed was allergic to these sleeping pills, which was why she almost stopped breathing, and why she almost died." (Line 10) People can be <u>allergic</u> to all of the following items *except*:
- p) foods
- q) animals
- r) medicines
- (s) other people

What are some reactions people can have if they are allergic to something?

_____

5) "My financial situation is none of your business." (Line 37) <u>None of your business</u> could be an appropriate answer to which of the following questions?
- s) What time is it?
- t) How much money do you make?
- u) Where is Birch Avenue?
- v) When does the bus arrive?

Why would someone say "none of your business?"

_____

6) "They give me an allowance of $200 a week, so I have no reason to steal their money." (Line 39) Choose the best word to complete the series.
parents → <u>allowance</u> → child : boss → _____ → worker
- v) congratulations
- u) salary
- w) friendship
- x) work

What does allowance mean?

_____

7) "You didn't call your fiancé?" (Line 69) In which series of relationships does <u>fiancé</u> belong?
- z) father → _____ → great-grandfather
- a) co-worker → _____ → boss
- b) boyfriend → _____ → husband
- c) stranger → _____ → friend

8) "He and some partners are building some condominiums in Springfield, Virginia." (Line 83) A condo, or <u>condominium</u>, is a(n) _____ that someone _____.
- m) room; rents
- n) office building; sells
- o) house; makes bigger
- p) apartment; buys

9) "Allison confirmed what the others had said—that only Evan, Nancy, Judith, and Lucia had keys to the bedroom, and that only Evan, Nancy, and Judith knew the combination to the safe." (Line 92) If you <u>confirm</u> what someone else said, then you:
- o) say something similar
- p) say something different
- q) answer a different question
- r) don't say anything

10) "Miguel lives in this house, and there is no sign that anyone broke into the house, so he is a suspect." (Line 105) The *opposite* of <u>break in</u> is:
   w) repair
   x) become rich
   y) enter with permission
   z) start a relationship

11) "Last week, the Reeds asked me to move out of their house by the end of the month." (Line 124) To <u>move out</u> means:
   k) to pay money for something
   l) to clean
   m) to improve something by fixing it
   n) to leave permanently

12) "It doesn't take special medical knowledge to crush some pills and put them in tea." (Line 161) To <u>crush</u> means:
   c) to buy
   d) to break into small pieces
   e) to make something more dangerous
   f) to put many pieces together

B. Comprehension Questions

13) In this chapter we learn about Sofia, Ellie's twelve year-old

   _____

14) Which of the following is *not* true about Kevin Reed on the night his parents were drugged?
   k) He says he played video games until midnight.
   l) He says he heard a strange noise from the third floor.
   m) He says he went to the movies with his friends until about 7:00 p.m.
   n) He says he ate dinner with his family.

15) Which of the following statements can we guess about Ellie?
   l) She probably lets her daughter watch a lot of TV.
   m) She probably gives Sofia a small allowance or no allowance.
   n) The Reed investigation is probably her first case.
   o) She probably has a poor relationship with her mother.

16) Why would Allison *probably* feel uncomfortable talking to Ted Quenton about her father's condominium project?
   a) Talking about money with one's future father-in-law is uncomfortable.
   b) Mr. Quenton does not have enough money to invest in the project.
   c) Allison doesn't know much about engineering or architecture.
   d) Derrick Quenton would get angry with her.

17) Which character or characters say that they were alone in their rooms at 9:30 p.m.?
   g) Allison
   h) Miguel
   i) Kevin
   j) both Miguel and Kevin

18) According to Miguel, who told him that there were crushed sleeping pills in the Reeds' tea?
   a) Allison
   b) a police officer
   c) Lucia
   d) Judith

19) Why does Allison get angry when Ellie asks her if Miguel might be guilty?
   e) Allison thinks that her brother, Kevin, is probably guilty, not Miguel.
   f) Allison thinks that Miguel is a suspect because he doesn't have much money.
   g) Ellie only asks questions about Miguel.
   h) Allison thinks that Miguel might be guilty, but is afraid to tell Ellie.

20) So far, Miguel is the only person who has a

   M _ _ _ _ V (e) to commit the crime.

   What is it?

   _____

Now, go back to page 27 and fill in the puzzle answers to find out what Miguel said.

A. Police Briefing

Get into small groups and select a chief detective. The chief detective will lead group discussions, and make sure all members are participating.

1. Check your Chapter 2 puzzle answers with your group.

2. Discuss the evidence. Use your Detective's Notebook to complete the box.

Whereabouts and Motives: Do we know where these suspects were at the time of the crime? What is a possible motive for each? If you are not sure, mark X.

Name	Whereabouts	Possible Motive
Judith		
Lucia		
Kevin		
Allison		
Miguel		

B. **Listen to the CD**

You will hear a message from the doctor at the crime lab, telling Ellie details about the drugged tea. After you listen, answer the questions.

1. Where is Dr. Henry? What time is it?

_____

2. What do Sleepinol pills look like? Mention the size, shape, color, and printing.

_____

3. Does Dr. Henry think that the criminal was trying to kill the Reeds? Explain.

_____

C. Think Ahead

This kind of story, or genre, is known by many names, for example "detective mystery," "crime thriller," "whodunit," etc. With your group, discuss what you know about "whodunits".

1. Name several "whodunit" movies that you have seen or books that you have read.

_____

2. Check the common characteristics of "whodunits":

☐ The hero falls in love with someone, but they must break up in the end.

☐ There is a group of suspects.

☐ The hero saves the world.

☐ The hero uses magic to solve the crime.

☐ The hero uses clues to solve the crime.

3. Think of three other characteristics of "whodunits," then discuss.

- _____
- _____
- _____

D. Quiz

Complete the quiz. You may use your Detective's Notebook, but close this book.

Pre-reading

Previously in *Whodunit... Three Interviews*

The following panels show three important events from Chapter 2. Order and caption each panel.

Chapter 3 : **The Hospital**

In this chapter, Ellie questions Judith Reed again. Then she talks to the two victims, Evan and Nancy Reed, at the hospital where they are recovering. She discovers that some of the suspects have been lying to her . . .

- **Answer these pre-reading questions alone or with a partner. If you don't know the answer, guess.**

1. Why is Ellie angry with Judith Reed?

   _____

2. Judith Reed bought a very valuable stamp called "The Inverted Eagle." There is a picture of it on page 34. Why are some stamps so valuable?

   _____

3. What are three questions that a police detective might ask the <u>victims</u> of a crime?

   Q1: _____

   Q2: _____

   Q3: _____

Chapter 3

The Hospital

Ellie watched Judith Reed walk slowly toward her down the long hallway. She stayed in her chair, staring at the older woman.

"Is there something you would like to tell me, Ms. Reed?" Ellie asked coldly.

"I… I don't know what you mean," Judith stammered.

"Ms. Reed, the fastest way to anger a police detective is to lie to her during an investigation." Ellie stood up, and now seemed to tower over Judith, even though they were the same height.

Judith dropped her cane, put her hands up to her face, and cried, "I know it was wrong to lie, but I was just trying to protect him. Yes, I gave the combination to my grandson, but I know he didn't drug his parents. He wouldn't do that!"

"You…," started Ellie, before realizing what Judith had said. "You gave the safe combination to Kevin? I called you in here because you gave it to Miguel!"

The older woman put her hands on the nearest chair, and Ellie helped her sit down. "I forgot that I gave it to Miguel," Judith said. "When you get to be my age, you sometimes forget things." She paused, and Ellie asked Yokota to get Judith a glass of water.

"Tell me everything," Ellie urged.

"You have to understand that I am an old woman. The safe is over the bed, and you have to stand on the bed to open it. If I stand on the bed I could fall. Usually I wait for my son or Nancy to open the safe for me, but there were two times when they weren't home and I didn't want to wait."

"When?" Ellie asked impatiently.

"The first time was about a month ago. I purchased a very beautiful stamp, a 2-cent George Washington from 1898. Evan and Nancy were away for the weekend, and I was afraid I would lose the stamp. Kevin was home, so I told him the combination and asked him to open the safe for me. I told him not to tell his parents. He promised that he would never open the safe again. I trust my grandson, Detective Koo."

Yokota returned with the water. Ellie turned to him and said, "Now two Reeds have lied to me. Bring me Kevin, please."

Judith sipped her water and continued. "Then, four days ago, I went to an auction and bought the prize of my collection, a 1920 Inverted Eagle stamp. The normal 1920 Eagle stamps are not very special, but the Inverted Eagles are extremely valuable. By accident, about 900 of the stamps were printed with the image of the eagle completely inverted. These rare stamps are worth a lot of money because the eagle is upside-down. Others have spent as much as $12,000 for one, but I got mine for only $10,000."

Ellie wondered how someone could spend $10,000, $1,000, or even $100 on a *sticker*, no matter how rare it was.

Judith continued, "I came home late from the auction. I thought that Nancy would be home, to put the stamp in the safe, but I couldn't find her anywhere. Miguel was reading in the kitchen. You have to understand, I had a $10,000 stamp in my purse. I just wanted to get it into the safe. He promised me that he would never open the safe again, or tell anyone that I gave him the combination."

"You don't seem very upset about the loss of your Inverted Eagle," Ellie said quickly.

"My son was drugged!" Judith yelled. "He could have died. Do you think I am worried about money or stamps at a time like this? What are you accusing me of?"

Ellie smiled playfully, hoping to anger Judith a little more. "Do you have insurance for your collection, Ms. Reed?"

"Of course," Judith scoffed.

"So," Ellie continued, "you won't actually lose any money from the loss of your collection."

Judith simply nodded, so Ellie continued, "Do you have an alibi for last night?"

"Am I a suspect?" snapped Judith. "Very well, detective. I ate dinner with my family. We finished at about 7:30. I went to my room and watched my favorite game show, Trivia King, until 8:00. Then I called my sister, Paula, who lives in Florida. We talked until 9:00 or so, and then I went to sleep. I am an old woman, Detective Koo. 9:00 is late enough for me. So no, I do not have an alibi for after 9:00."

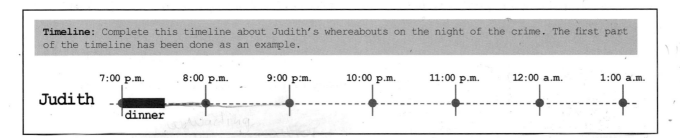

Timeline: Complete this timeline about Judith's whereabouts on the night of the crime. The first part of the timeline has been done as an example.

Just then, Yokota entered the room with Kevin. The elder Reed child looked annoyed to be back in the library. Ellie guessed that she was interrupting another round of video games.

"You lied to me, Kevin," began Ellie. "You said that you didn't know the safe combination."

"I didn't lie," Kevin said quickly, a smile forming on his lips. "I told you that my parents would never trust me with the combination. I never said that I didn't know the combination."

"You lied!" yelled Ellie, losing her temper. "You knew what I was asking. Why didn't you tell me the truth?"

"Because I'm not guilty," Kevin said. "I only opened the safe once, when my grandmother asked me to. To be honest, I don't even remember the combination."

Ellie laughed. "'To be honest?' You weren't honest before. Why should I believe you now?"

Kevin didn't answer. Ellie left him and Judith in the library. In the hallway, Yokota was touching the peach-colored paint on the wall. "This would be a nice color for my house," he mumbled. Then he looked at Ellie. "So, there are five people who know the combination. They could have told others. Anyone could have opened that safe."

"I don't know what to think," Ellie said, "except that I should meet Evan and Nancy. I want Allison, Kevin, Judith, Lucia, and Miguel all interviewed again. I want to know exactly where they were yesterday, and who they were with. I want officers out checking their stories. I also want this house searched from top to bottom. The contents of the safe might still be here."

Yokota nodded, writing down Ellie's instructions. "You're pretty angry," he observed.

She punched him gently on the shoulder. "I don't like being lied to during an investigation, Kaz."

"You don't have to worry about me," he said, pretending to be injured from the punch. "I'm as honest as they come."

"You're right," she said. "This *is* a nice color."

On the way to the hospital, Ellie reviewed her notes and thought about the case. Miguel had told her the truth about knowing the combination, but that didn't mean he was innocent. Miguel was intelligent—perhaps he suspected that Ellie already knew about the combination, and only told her the truth in order to seem honest. Kevin, on the other hand, did not appear to be very smart. Ellie knew, however, that people often were not as they appeared to be. Then there was Judith. She lied to Ellie, but could the old woman really climb onto the bed, open the safe, and carry away the contents?

In room 4123 of Georgetown Hospital, Nancy Reed was sleeping in one bed. Evan was whispering into a cell phone in the other. Ellie waited outside the room for a moment, hoping to hear some of Evan's conversation.

"Don't worry about me, Brian. There are three or four investors who are very excited about the project… Brian, I'm in the hospital. My wife almost died. Give me a few days to get the money together… You have nothing to worry about… Well, tell everyone that they will get their money in less than a week… Brian, you know me. You know you can trust me. Okay, I'll talk to you later."

Ellie waited for a few seconds and knocked on the door. "I'm Detective Eliana Koo," she said from the doorway. "I'm leading the investigation. Mr. Reed, do you feel well enough to answer a few questions?"

Evan looked very weak and pale. Ellie wondered if that was because of the drugging, or because of his phone conversation with 'Brian.' Evan was tall, thin, and losing his hair. He looked like a man who didn't go outside very often. "Of course," he answered. "What have you found out so far?"

Before Ellie could answer, Nancy Reed made a low noise and turned over. Seconds later she opened her eyes and sat up in bed. She had a tube coming out of her arm, and was receiving fluids from a bag. Her eyes were red, her hair uncombed, and her movements slow. Despite all of that, Ellie could see that she was a very attractive woman. She was physically fit and looked younger than her fifty years. Ellie introduced herself to Nancy Reed. Then she told both Reeds what she had discovered so far. She saved the most interesting fact for the end.

"Mr. and Mrs. Reed, did you know that both Kevin and Miguel knew the combination to the safe?"

"What?" they cried out together.

"Your mother told them, Mr. Reed." Ellie explained when and why Judith told Kevin and Miguel the combination.

"I can't believe she did that," yelled Nancy, looking at her husband. She suddenly looked much healthier. "Detective Koo, I can tell you right now who did this to us."

Ellie was surprised, and asked Nancy to continue.

"It was that Miguel," said Nancy. "Do you know that we asked him to move out? Do you know why? Last week I saw him leaving my daughter's room, and do you know what he had in his hand? Her watch, her favorite watch. I didn't say anything to him, and I didn't say anything to Allison, but I decided that I wanted him out of the house. My husband agreed. That's why Miguel did this to us."

Ellie wrote Nancy's suspicions down in her notebook. "Mr. Reed, do you agree with your wife? Do you think Miguel could be guilty?"

Evan Reed sighed and said, "I don't know. Maybe. I've always liked Miguel, but it's possible, especially since he knew the combination to the safe."

Ellie sensed that he wanted to say more. "But?"

"I hate to say it," he said, "but I also think that our son might have a motive."

"Evan!" cried Nancy.

"Kevin and I had a big fight just a few days ago. I told him that he was wasting his life, and that he had to get a job before the summer was over. I told him that, starting in September, we wouldn't be giving him an allowance."

"You did?" Nancy asked, sitting up straight in her bed. "I didn't know that."

"It was between Kevin and me. He was angry, detective."

Ellie frowned, realizing that Kevin had lied to her yet again.

"Mr. Reed, when was the last time you opened the safe?" Ellie asked.

"Let's see. About two weeks ago, when I helped Nancy take some of her cash out."

Her cash. "Mrs. Reed, the money in the safe was yours?"

Nancy nodded. "Evan and I keep our money separate. Most of his money is being used for his condominium project. The money and the jewelry in the safe were mine."

"And when was the last time that you opened the safe?" Ellie asked.

Nancy thought about it for a moment and answered, "With my husband, about two weeks ago."

"And can you tell me what happened last night?"

Mr. Reed answered, "I got out of the shower, and my tea was on my bedside table. I put on my pajamas, got into bed, and opened the book I'm reading. Nancy was in the bathroom, but she came out and got into bed a few seconds after I did. I sipped my tea a couple of times, and that is the last thing I remember. I woke up in the ambulance."

"Mrs. Reed, what about you?"

Nancy Reed rubbed her eyes. "Lucia brought the tea in around 9:30. It was too hot, so I set it on the table and kept reading. When Evan got out of the shower, I went to the bathroom and brushed my hair, like I do every night. Then I went back to bed and started drinking the tea. I remember that I started to feel sick, so I set my book on the table and tried to get up to go to the bathroom. But I felt too sick to get up, so I just lay there. That is the last thing I remember until I woke up here in the hospital."

"Mrs. Reed, did you know before today that you were allergic to your husband's sleeping pills?"

Nancy Reed's face turned white, and she whispered, "No, I didn't know. I can't believe I almost died. I can't believe that he almost killed me."

"Mr. Reed, where do you keep your sleeping pills?"

"In our bathroom, usually. But I refilled my prescription just a few days ago. Lucia picked up the pills for me." Evan frowned, looking embarrassed. "They were in the kitchen for a couple of days. I kept forgetting to take them upstairs."

Just then Ellie's cell phone rang. She excused herself and dashed into the hallway.

"Ellie, I'm glad I'm not standing next to you right now," Yokota said.

"Uh-oh. Why not?"

"Because I know how you feel about lying, and my shoulder is still sore."

Ellie sighed. "Who lied to me now?"

Yokota began, "I think we have a new motive..."

130

135

140

145

150

155

160

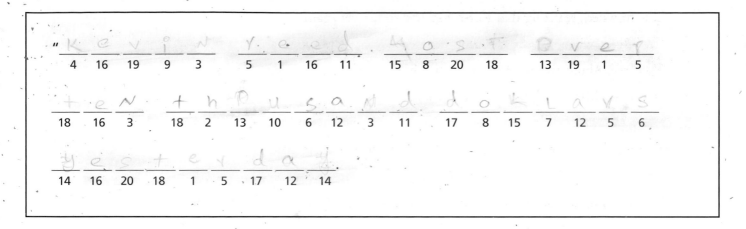

Ellie was very confused. "At the movies?"

"He said he went to movies," Yokota said, "but that was another lie. He went with some friends to the horse racing track,"

Ellie's temper began to flare again. She didn't know if Kevin was guilty, but she was sure that she didn't like him very much.

"He emptied his bank accounts and borrowed from his friends," Yokota continued, "but luck was not on his side."

"Apparently not," Ellie said. "We, however, now have another motive."

Instructions:

To discover what Yokota said, answer the following vocabulary and comprehension questions. After you have answered all of the questions, use the letters of the correct responses and the circled letters to solve the puzzle on page 39.

A. Vocabulary Questions

1) "By accident, about 900 of the stamps were printed with the image of the eagle completely inverted." (Line 35) Look at the picture on page 34. What does <u>inverted</u> mean?
   - e) reversed
   - f) broken
   - g) enlarged
   - h) funny

2) "These rare stamps are worth a lot of money because the eagle is upside-down." (Line 35) Which one of the following is <u>rare</u>?
   - g) a police car with a siren
   - h) a crime scene with children playing
   - i) a criminal with a motive
   - j) a detective with a badge

   What does rare mean?

   _____ not often _____

3) "Do you have insurance for your collection, Ms. Reed?" (Line 48)

   An <u>insurance</u> company will give you

   M _ (N) _ _ if your insured objects

   are stolen.

4) "'Am I a suspect?' snapped Judith." (Line 53) If you <u>snap</u>, then you say something _____ because you are _____.
   - i) slowly; calm
   - j) quietly; nervous
   - k) quickly; angry
   - l) many times; confused

5) "'You lied!' yelled Ellie, losing her temper." (Line 62)

   What emotion is associated with <u>losing one's</u>

   <u>temper</u>? A N g e (r).

6) "She punched him gently on the shoulder." (Line 76) In which sport do participants usually <u>punch</u> their opponents?
   - q) volleyball
   - r) baseball
   - s) boxing
   - t) tennis

7) "There are three or four investors who are very excited about the project." (Line 89) An <u>investor</u> is someone who _____ a company or project by _____.
   - k) destroys; stealing money
   - l) supports; lending money
   - m) starts; finding money
   - n) volunteers for; working hard

8) "What have you found out so far?" (Line 98)

   Another word for <u>find out</u> is:

   D _ S C _ (O) V e r .

9) "Evan Reed sighed and said, 'I don't know. Maybe.'" (Line 119) To <u>sigh</u> means to:
   - g) close your eyes sleepily
   - h) clear your throat angrily
   - i) breathe noisily
   - j) whisper quietly

10) "Ellie frowned, realizing that Kevin had lied to her yet again." (Line 129) The *opposite* of <u>frown</u> is:
    - r) relax
    - s) speak
    - t) sit down
    - u) smile

11) "I sipped my tea a couple of times, and that is the last thing I remember." (Line 140)

    <u>To sip</u> means to take a small

    (D) r i n k .

12) "Nancy Reed rubbed her eyes." (Line 143) In which of these situations would you *not* use the word <u>rub</u> ?
   y) "I rubbed his shoulders to give him a massage."
   z) "I rubbed the lamp with a towel to clean it."
   a) "I rubbed the door so that my friend would hear me."
   b) "I rubbed my foot after I stepped on a sharp rock."

What does it mean to rub something?

to move on surface of
something

B. Comprehension Questions

13) What *surprising* information does Judith give Ellie?
   n) that she gave Miguel the safe combination
   o) that she gave Kevin the safe combination
   p) that the money in the safe belonged to Nancy
   q) that the stamp collection belonged to her (Judith)

14) The following statements about Inverted Eagle stamps are true *except*:
   y) that they were printed in 1898
   z) that they contain an error
   a) that people pay more than $10,000 for them
   b) that there were only about 900 printed

15) Which of the following statements can we guess about Ellie?
   i) She probably dislikes Yokota.
   j) She probably believes what everyone tells her.
   k) She probably doesn't like to make jokes.
   l) She probably feels comfortable telling others what to do.

16) Why does Ellie hesitate before entering Evan and Nancy's hospital room?
   e) She wants to listen to Evan's phone conversation.
   f) She isn't sure if Evan and Nancy are sleeping.
   g) She wants to look through her notebook first.
   h) She needs to make an important phone call first.

17) Nancy Reed made all of these statements to Ellie except:
   a) "The money and the jewelry in the safe were mine."
   b) "I remember that I started to feel sick, so I set my book on the table and tried to get up to go to the bathroom."
   c) "I can't believe that he [Miguel] almost killed me."
   d) "He [Kevin] and I had a big fight just a few days ago."

18) Both Nancy and Evan last opened their safe
   (T) w o w e e k s earlier.

19) Why is the information that Evan gives about his sleeping pills important?
   t) Lucia was the only other person to handle the sleeping pills.
   u) The sleeping pills were stolen out of Evan's bathroom.
   v) Anyone who was in the kitchen could have taken some of the pills.
   w) Nancy knew that she was allergic to Evan's sleeping pills.

20) Who was surprised to learn that Kevin and Miguel knew the safe combination?
   q) Evan
   r) Nancy
   s) both Evan and Nancy
   t) neither Evan nor Nancy

Now, go back to page 39 and fill in the puzzle answers to find out what Yokota said.

A. Police Briefing

Get into small groups and select a chief detective. The chief detective will lead group discussions, and make sure all members are participating.

1. Check your Chapter 3 puzzle answers with your group.

2. Discuss the evidence and complete the box below.

What new facts did Ellie discover in this chapter? Are there any new suspects? Any new clues? What do you think about them?

New Evidence	What do you think?

B. **Listen to the CD**

You will hear Officer Yokota interviewing one of Kevin's friends. After you listen, answer the questions.

1. Which questions did Yokota ask to prove that Paul was lying? Select two questions:

   ☐ What time did the movie start?   ☐ What movie did you see?

   ☐ How much did the movie cost?   ☐ Did you eat popcorn?

   ☐ What was the movie about?   ☐ How did the movie end?

2. What happened in the ninth race at Northwood Track? Be specific.

   _____

3. Is Paul a good liar? Why or why not? Discuss.

   _____

C. Think Ahead

There are now two main suspects, Miguel and Kevin. Discuss the positives and negatives of each, and discuss who is most likely to be the robber.

Kevin

Positives	Negatives

Miguel

Positives	Negatives

Who is most likely to be the robber, and why, according to your group?

_____

D. Quiz

Complete the quiz. You may use your Detective's Notebook, but close this book.

Previously in *Whodunit... The Hospital*

The following panels show three important events from Chapter 3. Order and caption each panel.

....

Chapter 4 : The Suspect

In this chapter, the police find the stolen items. Ellie arrests one of the suspects, but discovers that there are still more secrets to be revealed. One of them involves a hidden romance.

• **Answer these pre-reading questions alone or with a partner. If you don't know the answer, guess.**

1. Nancy and Evan Reed, the victims, suspect two different people of drugging and robbing them. Who does each suspect, and why?

   Nancy suspects _____ because _____.

   Evan suspects _____ because _____.

2. Ellie discovers that Lucia lied to her. What do you think she lied about?

   _____

3. Who do you think will be arrested for drugging and robbing the Reeds, and why?

   _____

Chapter 4
The Suspect

Crime Talk: attorney, evidence, fingerprint, frame, suspect, under arrest, victim

The time was 3:00 p.m., but Kevin, of course, was home. Ellie pulled her car into the Reeds' 1
long driveway for the second time that day. This time, however, she knew exactly where to go. Kevin
lied to her about knowing the safe combination, his financial situation, and his activities on the day
of the crime. Ellie was looking forward to taking him down to the police station and questioning him
there. She was sure that there were more lies to discover.   5

Ellie's cell phone rang as she was stepping out of her car.

"Ellie," said Yokota. "You'd better get back to the Reed house right away."

"I'm right outside," she told her friend. "I'm here to pick up Kevin Reed and take him to the
station."

Yokota sighed and said, "You might change your mind after you see what I'm looking at. I'm   10
in Miguel's room, on the first floor."

Inside the Reed house, Ellie walked through the kitchen and past Lucia's bedroom to reach
Miguel's modest room. There were no knick-knacks or pictures on the wall, only a desk, a bed, a
closet, and a lot of books. Yokota and another officer were standing near the bed, looking down at a
pile of items that Ellie recognized immediately.   15

"You found them!" she exclaimed, already getting out a pair of gloves. "All of it is here—the jewelry, the cash, the stamps. Where were they?"

"Officer Wells here found the contents of the safe," said Yokota, smiling proudly. "Tell her."

Ellie recognized Natalie Wells from the Reeds' bedroom, earlier. She was a rookie officer and looked as nervous as a criminal. "I found the items here in this room, ma'am. Up there." 20

Ellie looked up and saw an open heating vent located high on the wall above the bed. The panel that covered the vent was swinging open. Ellie climbed onto the bed, careful not to tip over the items that were resting on it. "It was all in here?" she asked.

"Yes, ma'am," Wells said enthusiastically.

The vent was now empty. Officer Wells was clearly very pleased with herself for finding the 25 stolen items, but Ellie wondered why the thief chose such an obvious place to hide them. Perhaps he or she hadn't had time to take them out of the house—or maybe the thief wasn't as smart as Ellie thought.

Ellie climbed back down and patted Wells on the back. "Well done, officer," she said. "Please dust the vent and the items for fingerprints. I want to know everyone who touched the wall, the 30 jewelry, the cash, and the stamps."

Officer Wells dashed out of the room. Ellie leaned over the bed to inspect the items. The jewelry was all inside a wooden case, which Ellie carefully opened. She counted eight necklaces, six bracelets, and eleven rings—the exact amount that Nancy reported missing. She then counted the money. There were eight bundles of hundred-dollar bills. A quick estimate told Ellie that all $80,000 35 were present. Finally she examined the stamps. All thirteen stamps were inside plastic covers, to protect them from damage. Some stamps were attached to envelopes, others not. On top of the pile was Judith's prized stamp, the Inverted Eagle. The name of the auction house and the date of purchase were stamped on its plastic cover.

Under the stamps, however, Ellie found one more item—a woman's watch. The back of the 40 watch was engraved with the words "For Our Lovely Daughter." This was Allison's watch, the one that Nancy Reed told her about.

"Where is Miguel now?" Ellie asked Yokota.

"In class. He is supposed to be home at about 6:00."

"We can't wait that long. Let's pick him up."

Yokota was silent, and Ellie thought she knew why.

"I don't know if he did it," Ellie said, "but the items were found in his room. Maybe someone put the items in his room to frame Miguel, but we have to follow the evidence."

"I know," Yokota said, "but I like that kid. I hope he wasn't stupid enough to do this."

Ellie didn't say anything, but she shared Yokota's hope. She respected Miguel for earning a scholarship to Georgetown, and hoped he was innocent. Nevertheless, she had a job to do, even if she didn't want to do it.

"Kevin is up in his room, if you want to speak with him first," Yokota added.

"It will have to wait," Ellie said regretfully. "But make sure an officer watches him closely. I want to know his every step."

Ellie stepped out of Miguel's bedroom, only to find herself face to face with Lucia.

"Why were you in…," began the surprised housekeeper. "What's going on?"

Ellie explained that they had found the missing items in Miguel's room, and Lucia burst into tears.

45

50

55

"I'm sorry, Ms. Deza," Ellie said, sincerely.

"You don't understand," begged Lucia, leaning against the wall for support. "Miguel is not a criminal. He is a good boy. He works so hard in school, but always has time to help me do the laundry, wash the dishes, make tea in…" Lucia stopped talking suddenly, and looked down to the floor.

"Make tea?" Ellie asked. She remembered that Lucia had been very nervous when they'd met in the Reeds' bedroom. "Ms. Deza, your son helped you make the Reeds' tea last night, didn't he? You lied to me when you said you were alone in the kitchen."

Lucia turned away from Ellie and walked into her bedroom. She sat on her bed and put her face in her hands. "All right, I lied. I was tired, and Miguel said he would make the tea for me. But listen, Miguel is a good boy. He would never hurt anybody. You have to believe me."

Ellie felt sorry for Lucia, even though she and her son had lied about who made the tea. She left the housekeeper alone in her room, but told an officer to look after her.

Ellie decided to take Yokota's black and white police car to pick Miguel up. Yokota flipped the keys to her, saying, "We both know you're the better driver." Inside the car, Yokota took out a copy of Miguel's class schedule and mumbled to them both, "Okay, today is Thursday. Today is the only day he has a late afternoon class. It starts in about fifteen minutes. He should be in the Medical and Science Building on the north side of campus, off Reservoir Road."

Ellie was on 35th Street, and made a left on Reservoir Road. "Wait a minute," she said suddenly. "Did you say that today is the only day Miguel has a late class?"

"Let's see. That's right."

"He told me that he had class until 7:00 yesterday. He lied to me about helping his mom and about his schedule. Is anyone telling me the truth?"

Yokota, wisely, kept quiet.

Ellie parked the car across the street from the campus, right in front of a large No Parking sign. That was one advantage of the black and white police car.

She and Yokota didn't have to search for long. They found Miguel sitting on a bench outside the Medical and Science Building, talking with a classmate. He saw them coming and excused himself. They met halfway across the courtyard in front of the red brick building.

Ellie noticed that several students were watching them. She said to Miguel, "I'd like to do this quietly, if that's all right with you."

Miguel looked confused for a moment. Then his eyes opened wide with understanding. He sighed, and said, "After you, detective."

The three of them crossed the street, and Miguel entered the backseat without any argument.

"Miguel Deza," began Yokota with a frown on his face, "you are under arrest for drugging and robbing Evan and Nancy Reed. You have the right to an attorney…"

Miguel waited for Yokota to finish speaking, and said, "Detective, this is a mistake. I swear to you that I'm innocent."

Ellie wanted to believe him, but wasn't sure what to think. "I recommend that you don't say anything without an attorney," she said.

"I don't need an attorney. I'm innocent."

Ellie started the car and waited for the Reservoir Road traffic to clear. "You lied, Miguel. You lied to me when you didn't tell me that you prepared the Reeds' tea last night. Didn't you think that was an important detail?"

"But I…" began Miguel, his voice breaking nervously. "All right, I should have told you. The truth is that after I made the tea, I went to the bathroom and then went to find my mom. Anyone could have drugged the tea while it was in the kitchen. I'm sorry I didn't tell you, but I knew how bad it would look, and I never thought you would…"

"Find out?" Ellie asked, finishing his sentence for him. "So, it's okay to lie if you think you won't get caught?"

"No, of course not," he mumbled. "I should have told you. Whenever I make Mrs. Reed's tea, I forget to add honey. She loves honey in her tea, and she complains to my mom when I forget. I should have known that you would find out. I'm sorry."

Miguel thought that Nancy had told Ellie about the tea, not Lucia. Ellie decided not to tell him the truth. "That wasn't the only lie, Miguel. You told me that you had class until 7:00 p.m. last night, but according to your schedule, your last class finished at 4:30 p.m."

Miguel was silent. In the rearview mirror, Ellie could see that he looked tired and angry. Finally he said, "Lying is wrong, but it doesn't make me a thief."

"You're right," Yokota said. "The problem is that we found the contents of the safe—the jewelry and the money and the stamps. Can you guess where we found them?"

Ellie was turning onto Wisconsin Avenue, but looked back in the mirror to see Miguel's expression. His mouth was open and his forehead was wrinkled, but Ellie couldn't read his emotions.

"In your room, Miguel," Ellie said, still watching his face. "Along with Allison Reed's watch. That's the problem. That's why you're under arrest."

"In my room?" he gasped. "That's impossible. Detective Koo, I swear I didn't steal anything. I swear."

"Not even Allison's watch?" Ellie asked.

Miguel was quiet for several seconds. "I didn't steal the watch," he finally said. "Allison gave it to me last week, but I lost it a couple days ago. I didn't tell her that I lost it because I was embarrassed." 125

Yokota turned in his seat and looked at Miguel. "Miguel, I saw the watch. It's a woman's watch. Why would Allison give you a watch that you would never wear?"

Miguel hesitated, then said, "Because she was leaving for college soon, and she wanted to give me something that was important to her." 130

"But why?" Ellie asked, turning the car into the police station. "Why would she do that?"

Miguel looked out the window at the police cars parked in front of the station, and said…

"a l l i s o n a n d i a r e i n
13 11 11 16 20 4 19   13 19 2   16   13 9 17   16 7

l o v e . w e ' v e b e e n d a t i n g
11 15 1 8   18 8 1 8   5 8 17 7   2 13 10 16 19 6

f o r t w o m o n t h s ."
12 15 9   10 18 4   14 15 7 10 3 20

Ellie glanced at Yokota and then looked at Miguel again in the mirror. "She is engaged to Derrick Quenton, Miguel."

Miguel sunk back into the seat and put his hands over his face, like his mother had. "She is engaged, but she doesn't love him. We always had a nice friendship, but when she came home from college this summer we realized that our feelings had changed. She was planning on breaking up with Derrick as soon as she returned to Brown. Now I don't know what's going to happen. And now, with me under arrest for drugging and robbing her parents…" 135

"Does anyone else know about your relationship?" Yokota asked. 140

"I haven't told anyone, and I don't think that she has."

Ellie parked the car. She smiled at Miguel, then turned to Yokota. "Officer Yokota, please take Miguel inside. I'm going to borrow your car."

END OF CHAPTER 4 END OF CHAPTER 4 END OF CHAPTER 4

Instructions:

To discover what Miguel said, answer the following vocabulary and comprehension questions. After you have answered all of the questions, use the letters of the correct responses and the circled letters to solve the puzzle on page 50.

A. Vocabulary Questions

1) "Inside the Reed house, Ellie walked through the kitchen and past Lucia's bedroom to reach Miguel's modest room." (Line 13) Another word for modest is:
   - u) large
   - v) simple
   - w) old
   - x) crowded

   simple

2) "She was a rookie officer and looked as nervous as a criminal." (Line 19) A rookie is *not*:
   - b) intelligent
   - c) lucky
   - d) experienced
   - e) honest

3) "Ellie looked up and saw an open heating vent located high on the wall above the bed." (Line 21) All of the following statements about vents in homes are true *except*:
   - h) They are usually painted bright colors.
   - i) They are a way for air to move in and out of a room.
   - j) The usually have a cover on them.
   - k) They are usually too small for a person to enter.

4) "Ellie climbed onto the bed, careful not to tip over the items that were resting on it." (Line 22)

   Another verb that means tip over is:

   K n (o) c k over.

5) "Officer Wells was clearly very pleased with herself for finding the stolen items, but Ellie wondered why the thief chose such an obvious place to hide them." (Line 26) Ellie thinks the vent is an obvious place because it is:
   - b) easy to find
   - c) difficult to find
   - d) dangerous to open
   - e) safe to open

6) "Officer Wells dashed out of the room." (Line 32) If you dash out of a place, then you leave there _____.
   - f) safely
   - g) quickly
   - h) accidentally
   - i) slowly

7) "Ellie leaned over the bed to inspect the items." (Line 32)

   Another word for inspected, which appears in the same paragraph, is

   E x a m (n) e _ .

8) "There were eight bundles of hundred-dollar bills. A quick estimate told Ellie that all $80,000 were present." (Line 35) How many hundred-dollar bills were in each bundle?
   - b) 8
   - c) 10
   - d) 80
   - e) 100

9) "Ellie explained that they had found the missing items in Miguel's room, and Lucia burst into tears." (Line 58)

   To burst into tears means to c _ (r) y suddenly.

10) "Inside the car, Yokota took out a copy of Miguel's class schedule..." (Line 73) A class schedule probably includes all of the following information *except*:
    - s) the numbers of the classrooms
    - t) the student's area of study
    - u) the days of the week
    - v) the names of the classes

11) "Inside the car, Yokota took out a copy of Miguel's class schedule and mumbled to them both, 'Okay, today is Thursday.'" (Line 73) A person who <u>mumbles</u> a lot might hear:

j) "Slow down, you're talking too fast."
k) "Shhh, you're so loud."
l) "Sorry, can you repeat that?"
m) "Relax. Why are you so excited?"

What does it mean to mumble?

_____ to _____

12) "I swear to you that I am innocent." (Line 94) Miguel uses the word <u>swear</u> in this sentence because:

c) he is using bad language
d) he is talking to his attorney
e) he wants to make Ellie angry
f) he wants Ellie to believe him

B. Comprehension Questions

13) Which one of the following is *not* true about the items stolen from the safe?

z) The jewelry was inside a wooden box.
a) Yokota found them in the heating vent.
b) All of the jewelry, money, and stamps were found.
c) The stamps were found in individual plastic covers.

14) Who gave Allison the watch that was found with the items from the safe?

m) her parents
n) Miguel
o) Derrick Quenton
p) Kevin

15) Which one of the following statements is *probably* true about Ellie?

l) She is unfamiliar with the Georgetown section of Washington DC
m) She drives faster than the speed limit.
n) She likes to embarrass people.
o) She tries to separate her emotions from her job.

16) What lie did Lucia tell Ellie?

h) that Miguel had classes until 7:00 p.m.
i) that she made the Reeds' tea on the night of the crime
j) that Miguel helped her with the laundry
k) that she didn't know the safe combination

17) Miguel often forgets to add

H o n (e) y to Mrs. Reed's tea.

18) In Miguel's room, why does Ellie wonder if the thief is intelligent?

t) All of the money was still there.
u) The items were still in the house.
v) Officer Wells is only a rookie officer.
w) The items were easy to find.

19) Why does Ellie watch Miguel in the rearview mirror?

l) to frighten him
m) because she is afraid of him
n) to watch his emotions
o) to make him feel more comfortable

20) Thur(s)day is the only day that Miguel has a late class.

Why is Ellie surprised by this information?

_____

Now, go back to page 50 and fill in the puzzle answers to find out what Miguel said.

A. Police Briefing

Get into small groups and select a chief detective. The chief detective will lead group discussions, and make sure all members are participating.

1. Check your Chapter 4 puzzle answers with your group.

2. Discuss the evidence and complete the box below.

Ellie uncovered some new lies in this chapter. Who has lied to Ellie so far? What were the lies?

Name	Lie
Lucia	Lied about making tea

B. Listen to the CD

TRACK 4

You will hear Officer Yokota interviewing Miguel about his relationship with Allison. After you listen, answer the questions.

1. Why did Miguel laugh when Yokota asked him about going to school with Allison?

_____

2. Why is Allison unhappy with Derrick? Mention two reasons.

_____

3. After listening to Miguel's story, do you think he drugged the Reeds? Why or why not? Discuss.

_____

C. Think Ahead

What other lies will Ellie discover? Choose three of these characters and make a good guess about a lie that each one may have told.

> Evan   Nancy   Kevin   Allison   Miguel   Judith   Lucia

1. _____ lied about _____.

2. _____ lied about _____.

3. _____ lied about _____.

D. Quiz

Complete the quiz. You may use your Detective's Notebook, but close this book.

Chapter 5 : Pre-reading

Previously in *Whodunit... The Suspect*

The following panels show three important events from Chapter 4. Order and caption each panel.

....

Chapter 5 : Family Secrets

In this chapter, Ellie's daughter Sofia unknowingly gives her an idea about the case. The police also discover some shocking new facts about the Reed family. When there is money involved, nothing is as it seems.

• **Answer these pre-reading questions alone or with a partner. If you don't know the answer, guess.**

1. Family secrets are usually embarrassing facts that only members of the family are allowed to know. What kind of facts are often "kept in the family"?

   _____

   _____

   _____

2. Which of the above do you think may be the Reeds' secret?

   _____

3. Do you think Miguel is telling the truth about his relationship with Allison?   ☐ Yes   ☐ No
   Why?

   _____

   _____

Chapter 5

Family Secrets

Crime Talk: case, clue, fingerprint, proof

Ellie parked illegally for the second time that day, knowing that in Yokota's black and white police car she wouldn't get a parking ticket. Climbing the stairs two at a time, she reached the third floor of her apartment building in just a few seconds. Her apartment was 304, but she kept walking and knocked on the door of 308. 1

A shadow moved under the door, and across the peep hole. Ellie was glad that Vi Nguyen didn't open the door to strangers. 5

The door opened. "Hello, neighbor," Vi said warmly. "Come in and take off your coat."

"You know me better than that, Vi," Ellie answered, following her neighbor into the apartment. "This coat is like my second skin."

Vi smiled. "I didn't expect you until 5:30. The girls are helping me make some cookies." 10

Ellie hated having to ask for another favor. "Actually, that's why I'm stopping by. I was hoping you could watch Sofia for a couple more hours."

Vi's daughter, Colleen, was the same age as Sofia, and attended the same summer camp at the elementary school. Vi was nice enough to pick up both of the girls at 4:00 p.m., when the camp day was finished. She also watched Sofia until Ellie got home from work. Ellie was grateful for her 15 neighbor's help.

"You're in luck," Vi said. "My husband and I are going to take our kids to the movies tonight. We can take Sofia, too, if you'd like."

Ellie leaned forward and gave her neighbor a little hug. "That would be perfect. I really owe you." 20

"Hi, mom!" Ellie heard from the kitchen. Seconds later Sofia was in the hallway, giving Ellie a much bigger hug. "Are you on a hot case?"

"A very hot one," Ellie said, tucking Sofia's curly hair behind her ears. "I'll be home when you get back from the movie, okay?"

Sofia grabbed Ellie's hand and looked into her eyes with her most loving expression. Ellie 25 recognized this look immediately.

"What do you want?" Ellie asked nervously.

"Nothing much," Sofia said, tilting her head in an effort to look as cute as possible. "Only that a couple of boys from the camp are going to the mall this Saturday. They asked Colleen and me if we wanted to go. Can I, mom? Please please please?" 30

Ellie had been fearing this moment for weeks, ever since Sofia and Colleen started talking about all of the cute boys in their camp.

"Let me think about it," she told her daughter, which brightened Sofia's face immediately. Usually when Ellie said that she would think about something, the answer was yes. "I would need to talk to these boys' parents, and I would want to drive you there and pick you up. We'll talk about it 35 tonight."

Sofia was obviously happy with that answer. She kissed her mother goodbye and ran back into the kitchen. Vi stepped back into the hallway.

"Boys," Vi said, half-smiling. "They want to go out with boys. Our lives are about to get much more complicated." 40

Ellie thought about her daughter on the way back to Birch Drive. *Boys,* she thought to herself.

Back in the Reed house, Ellie found Allison up in her room, crying on her bed. "It's impossible," she told Ellie, wiping her eyes. "It must be some kind of mistake. Miguel would never do this."

Ellie sat down at Allison's desk, still half-thinking about her own daughter. *Boys.* "Allison, I 45 checked your work schedule. You didn't work late last night, like you told me. Your shift ended at 4:30, just like Miguel's class. You were with him, weren't you?"

Allison blew her nose, then said, "We always meet on Tuesdays and Wednesdays outside the library. Sometimes we just sit. Sometimes we take a walk, or go out for some food. Yesterday we went to a coffee shop and talked about…" 50

"About your future," Ellie said, after Allison hesitated for several seconds. "About breaking up with Derrick."

Allison nodded and told Ellie the same story that Miguel had. She swore that she had not told anyone about her relationship with Miguel, not even her best friends.

Ellie looked over her notebook. "Miguel said that he stopped watching TV last night at about 8:30. You said that you started watching a movie at the same time." 55

It wasn't a question, but Allison understood. "We were together in the basement," Allison said shyly. "Kissing, talking. More kissing than talking, I guess."

"Until when?"

"About 9:15. Then he went to see if his mother needed any help." 60

And make your parents' tea, Ellie thought, writing down Allison's new version of her evening. "Allison, do you have any proof of your relationship with Miguel?"

Allison seemed to think it over for a few seconds. Then she stood up and pulled out a thin blue book from under her mattress. "This is my diary," she said, cautiously handing it over to Ellie. "I haven't told anyone about our relationship, but I wrote about it here." 65

Ellie opened the diary. The entries were dated, and Ellie soon found the entries from the last two months. Miguel's name appeared many times. After reading for a few minutes, she was convinced that Miguel and Allison were telling the truth about their relationship.

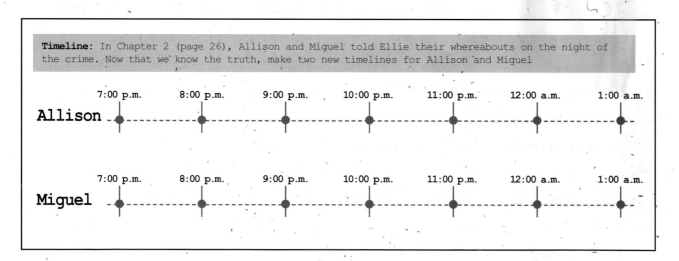

Timeline: In Chapter 2 (page 26), Allison and Miguel told Ellie their whereabouts on the night of the crime. Now that we know the truth, make two new timelines for Allison and Miguel

"I'm going to need to borrow your diary," Ellie said. "Have you showed it to anyone?"

"No way," Allison said, embarrassed. "Do you share your diary with anyone?" 70

Ellie smiled, thinking of the pink book she had found in Sofia's room. It had been difficult not to read her daughter's diary, but in the end she had done the right thing and put it back where she'd found it, unread.

"One more question," Ellie said. "Did you give your watch to Miguel?"

"Uh-huh," Allison said, nodding. "My parents gave it to me when I turned fourteen, and it's important to me. I wanted Miguel to keep it until we could be together again."

Ellie left Allison's room, passing Kevin's open door as she walked to the stairs. He was sitting in front of his TV, shooting aliens or monsters or something.

"I told you I was innocent," he yelled as she passed.

Ellie stopped, tempted to confront Kevin about the lies he had told, or at least say something cruel about losing $10,000 at the racetrack. She still wasn't convinced that Miguel was guilty, and privately hoped that Kevin was. She decided it was better to let Kevin think that he was safe. After all, confident people make more mistakes than cautious ones.

Officer Wells almost ran into Ellie as she reached the bottom of the stairs.

"Oh, detective, I'm sorry," she cried, looking frightened. "I did everything you asked. There were no fingerprints around the vent. Whoever put the items in there was probably wearing gloves. The items had plenty of fingerprints, and they are being identified now."

Ellie said, "I have one more item for you. This diary. I want all of the pages dusted for fingerprints. I want to know who opened it, and which pages they touched."

Wells tried to slip on a pair of rubber gloves, but accidentally put two of her fingers in the same hole. Ellie looked away, trying not to laugh. Finally Wells straightened the gloves out, took the diary from Ellie, and ran off as quickly as possible.

Ellie looked back up the stairs and decided to study the scene of the crime once more. There was yellow police tape blocking the Reeds' bedroom door, but Ellie ducked underneath and entered.

The room looked the same as it had that morning, except that the tea on the floor next to Nancy Reed's side of the bed had dried. Evan Reed's reading lamp was still on, and his wallet and watch were still beside it. It seemed odd to Ellie that Miguel would leave such an expensive watch on the table.

There was an important clue here in the bedroom. Ellie could feel it. But what?

She slipped off her shoes and set them on the bed. Then she stepped onto the bed in order to examine the safe. The mattress was very soft, and the whole bed rocked as Ellie walked across it. She could hear her shoes falling to the floor behind her. *I can see why Judith doesn't like to open the safe,* Ellie thought to herself. *It's dangerous up here.*

Standing near the wall now, with her feet by the Reeds' pillows, Ellie examined the painting that covered the wall safe. It was a large painting, and she had to step back to open it fully. Both the painting and the safe had been dusted for fingerprints. The results were not surprising — Evan's, Nancy's, Kevin's, and Miguel's.

Ellie carefully stepped off the bed, frustrated by her lack of ideas. Shoes on, she ducked back under the police tape, and was surprised to hear a voice to her left.

"Who's there?" she called out, peering into the dark library at the end of the hall, the room where she interviewed Kevin, Allison, and Miguel.   110

A lamp switched on, and Judith Reed appeared, sitting in the largest library chair. "Just an old woman. Don't shoot."

"Do you always sit alone in the dark?" Ellie asked, approaching Judith.

"It's a Reed tradition," Judith said, smiling with one corner of her mouth. "I do it, Evan does it. Even Nancy likes to sit here in the dark. It's very relaxing."   115

The sadness in Judith's voice was unmistakable. Ellie felt sorry for the older woman. "Did you hear that we found the missing items? Your Inverted Eagle was right on top of the pile."

Judith said quietly, "I almost lost my son today because I gave the safe combination to that boy. I have nothing to feel happy about."

Ellie tried to find some words of comfort, and was saved by the ringing of her cell phone. She   120
excused herself and answered the phone on the stairs. It was Evan Reed.

"So my wife was right?" he asked. "Is it true that you found the stolen items and arrested Miguel?"

"It's true," Ellie said, telling Evan about the heating vent.

"Well, I can't thank you enough, detective. It saddens me that Miguel would do this to us, but at   125
least we know the truth."

Ellie wasn't sure that all of the truth had been discovered, but accepted Evan's thanks. "Mr. Reed, do you know that Miguel and Allison have been dating all summer, and that Allison planned to break up with Derrick Quenton?" Ellie asked the question quickly, hoping to surprise Evan Reed and get an honest reaction.   130

"They have?" he cried out. "She was? Are you certain?"

"She told me herself."

Evan made a series of noises that sounded to Ellie like a car trying to start. Finally he said, "I can't believe this. I had no idea."

Ellie was going to ask him about Lucia Deza, and if they planned to keep her in their home,   135
when Evan called out, "Nancy, did you have any idea that Miguel and Allison were dating?"

Nancy's shocked cry was easy to hear, even over the telephone. "What are you talking about?" she shouted. "That's not possible!"

Evan tried to explain, but eventually Ellie had to talk to Nancy herself.

"It's true, Mrs. Reed. Both of them told me the same story."   140

"Detective Koo," Nancy said very seriously, "my daughter is going to marry Derrick Quenton. I hope that you will not spread any rumors that might jeopardize their relationship."

Ellie was annoyed by Nancy's tone of voice, but said calmly, "Mrs. Reed, I don't spread rumors. I find and report facts. If I were you, I would worry more about how your daughter is feeling than about her engagement."   145

Ellie had been walking while she talked. She was outside the Reed house when her conversation with Nancy Reed ended. At the same time, a black and white pulled into the driveway. Yokota stepped out of the passenger seat.

Yokota thanked the officer who had dropped him off, and turned just in time to catch his car keys.   150

"Nice catch," Ellie said.

"I'm old," answered her friend, "but not blind yet."

"Any news?"

"Lucia Deza is at the station. She contacted a lawyer for Miguel."

Yokota was smiling widely, and Ellie knew he had more to tell her. "And?"   155

"And," he said, "I've discovered one more Reed family secret...

" e v e n   R e e d   i s   b r o k e.
   17 14 8 3   1 17 17 18   19 5   13 1 20 7 17

   h e   l o s t   e v e r y t h i n g   i n
   15 17   4 20 5 16   17 14 17 1 9 16 15 19 3 10   19 3

   h i s   b u i l d i n g   P r o j e c t."
   15 19 5   13 2 19 4 18 19 3 10   11 1 20 12 17 6 16

Ellie stared at Yokota, surprised beyond words. "How is that possible? Look at this house. Look at all the things they have."

"All Nancy's," Yokota said, smiling. He seemed to be enjoying himself. "This house used to belong to her parents and is in her name. She made more money than him. They divide their accounts, keeping their money separate."   160

Ellie remembered talking to the Reeds in the hospital. The money in the safe was Nancy's, not Evan's. In fact, nothing from the safe was his. "What happened?"

"His condominium project has been a disaster. All of his partners have left him, and he has had one problem after another. For example, he had to stop construction because the land is too soft. He   165
can't start again until he pays his architect, Brian Schwartz, to change the plans. You should hear the angry message the architect left me."

Ellie remembered the conversation she overheard in the hospital, and thought back to Allison's conversation with her father. Evan had asked Allison to talk to Ted Quenton about investing in his project, but she said no.   170

"Kaz," she finally said, "suddenly I'm not so sure that Evan Reed is the *victim* of this crime."

END OF CHAPTER 5   END OF CHAPTER 5   END OF CHAPTER 5

Instructions:

To discover what Yokota said, answer the following vocabulary and comprehension questions. After you have answered all of the questions, use the letters of the correct responses and the circled letters to solve the puzzle on page 62.

A. Vocabulary Questions

1) "Ellie leaned forward and gave her neighbor a little hug." (Line 19) If someone or something is <u>leaning</u>, then it is:
    r) standing at an angle
    s) standing up taller
    t) standing up straighter
    u) jumping up off the ground

2) *"And make your parents' tea,* Ellie thought, writing down Allison's new version of her evening." (Line 61) When you give your <u>version</u> of something that happened, you are saying:
    t) what you read about the event
    u) what you know about the event
    v) what you wanted to happen
    w) the plan for the event

3) "'This is my diary,' she said, cautiously handing it over to Ellie." (Line 64)

    A <u>diary</u> is a personal

    J _ o _ u _ r _ n _ (_h_) _ a _ L .

    What type of information do people usually write in diaries?

    _____

4) "Ellie stopped, tempted to confront Kevin about the lies he had told, or at least say something cruel about losing $10,000 at the racetrack." (Line 80) If someone was <u>tempted</u> to do something, then he or she:
    j) wanted to do it, and probably did
    k) did not want to do it, but probably did
    l) wanted to do it, but probably did not
    m) did not want to do it, and probably did not

5) "Ellie stopped, tempted to confront Kevin about the lies he had told, or at least say something cruel about losing $10,000 at the racetrack." (Line 80) The *opposite* of <u>confront</u> is:
    s) avoid
    t) face
    u) understand
    v) challenge

6) "Ellie stopped, tempted to confront Kevin about the lies he had told, or at least say something cruel about losing $10,000 at the racetrack." (Line 80) Which one of the following is an example of <u>saying something cruel</u>?
    z) "The food needs just a little more salt."
    a) "You're really good at soccer."
    b) "I'm sorry, but I don't know the answer."
    c) "You look terrible today."

7) "She still wasn't convinced that Miguel was guilty, and privately hoped that Kevin was." (Line 81) If you are <u>convinced</u> that something is true, then:
    h) you need more evidence to know if it is true
    i) you don't care if it is true or not
    j) you are very doubtful that it is true
    k) you have enough evidence to believe it

8) "After all, confident people make more mistakes than cautious ones." (Line 83)

    Another word for <u>cautious</u> is

    C (_a_) _r_ _e_ _f_ _u_ _l_ .

9) "There was yellow police tape blocking the Reeds' bedroom door, but Ellie ducked underneath and entered the now empty room." (Line 94) In which situation might someone tell you to <u>duck</u>?
    x) You are about to fall into the water.
    y) A ceiling is very low.
    z) You are illegally entering a building.
    a) A person or animal is chasing you.

    What does it mean to duck?

    _____

10) "Ellie carefully stepped off the bed, frustrated by her lack of ideas." (Line 107) All of the following situations might <u>frustrate</u> you *except*:
    e) being confused about a homework problem
    f) losing your car keys
    g) finding money in your pocket
    h) getting lost in a big city

What does it mean to feel frustrated?

_____

11) "I hope that you will not spread any rumors that might jeopardize their relationship." (Line 142)

Another word for <u>rumors</u> is:

G o s s i (p).

12) "I hope that you will not spread any rumors that might jeopardize their relationship." (Line 142) If you <u>jeopardize</u> something, then you:
    g) find out more information about it
    h) protect it
    i) forget about it
    j) put it in danger

B. Comprehension Questions

13) In one word, what are *both* Ellie and Vi worried about? (b) o y s .

14) What did Allison lie to Ellie about?
    t) spending time with Miguel after work
    u) spending time with Miguel after talking to her father
    v) both (t) and (u)
    w) neither (t) nor (u)

15) Which one of the following statements can we guess about Ellie?
    g) She is probably married.
    h) She probably respects her daughter's privacy.
    i) She probably doesn't trust Vi Nguyen.
    j) She probably has allowed her daughter to go to the mall with boys in the past.

16) What does Ellie want Officer Wells to do with Allison's diary?
    q) to read the entries about Miguel
    r) to return it to Allison
    s) to use it to prove that Allison and Miguel are dating
    t) to dust it for fingerprints

17) Nancy is very worried about Allison's

E n g a g e m e (a) n t

to Derrick Quenton.

18) Why is Judith depressed when Ellie finds her sitting alone in the dark library?
    b) She really liked Miguel.
    c) The Inverted Eagle is in bad condition.
    d) She blames herself for the crime.
    e) Allison and Miguel were dating in secret.

19) Why doesn't Ellie talk to Kevin in this chapter?
    h) She now knows that he is innocent.
    i) She wants him to feel confident.
    j) She doesn't have time.
    k) He feels sad about what happened to his parents.

20) Ellie now knows all of the following information *except*:
    l) whose fingerprints are on the vent in Miguel's room
    m) whose fingerprints are on the safe
    n) whose fingerprints are on the painting that covers the safe
    o) whose fingerprints are on the items stolen from the safe

Now, go back to page 62 and fill in the puzzle answers to find out what Yokota said.

A. Police Briefing

Get into small groups and select a chief detective. The chief detective will lead group discussions, and make sure all members are participating.

1. Check your Chapter 5 puzzle answers with your group.

2. Discuss the evidence and complete the box below.

> What new facts did Ellie discover in this chapter? Are there any new suspects? Any new clues? What do you think about them?

New Evidence	What do you think?

B. **Listen to the CD**

You will hear a recorded voice message from the architect for Evan Reed's condominium project. He will talk about the problems with the project. After you listen, answer the questions.

1. Which of the following did Brian Schwartz do for the condominium project?

    ☐ ordered the building materials   OR   ☐ connected the electricity

    ☐ found buyers for the condos   OR   ☐ drew up all of the plans

    ☐ got the contracts   OR   ☐ looked for new investors

    ☐ moved the buildings by 100 m.   OR   ☐ hired the builders

2. What does Schwartz need to do to fix the problem of the soft land?

    _____

3. Do you think that Nancy Reed knows about Evan's financial problems? Why or why not? Discuss.

C. Think Ahead

At the end of Chapter 5, Ellie seems to have a strong feeling or guess—a 'hunch'—about who the criminal is. Does your team have any hunches? Discuss each character in turn.

Kevin

Allison

Miguel

Judith

Lucia

Evan

Nancy

D. Quiz

Complete the quiz. You may use your Detective's Notebook, but close this book.

Chapter 6 : Pre-reading

Previously in *Whodunit... Family Secrets*

The following panels show three important events from Chapter 5. Order and caption each panel.

Chapter 6 : The Arrest

In this final chapter, Ellie makes another arrest and finally solves the case. Was it a crime of greed, or a crime of love? Maybe it was a little of both.

• **Answer these pre-reading questions alone or with a partner. If you don't know the answer, guess.**

1. Officer Wells finds fingerprints in Allison's diary. Can you guess whose fingerprints?

   Wells will find _____'s fingerprints because _____

   _____.

2. The Inverted Eagle stamp is important in this chapter. Can you guess why?

   _____

3. Ellie finally solves the case. Who do you think is guilty, and why?

   _____

   _____

   _____

Chapter 6

The Arrest

Back at the police station, Ellie made a few phone calls. She learned that Evan Reed had   1
received several loans from Washington Bank, where he worked. However, most of that money was
now gone. His mother and children did not seem to know about his money problems. To make things
worse, he gave Judith money for expensive stamps, like the Inverted Eagle.

Sofia would be home in about forty-five minutes, probably hungry and eager to talk about her   5
Saturday at the mall. Ellie turned off her computer and got ready to go home. Officer Wells, folder in
hand, caught her just as she was leaving the station.

"Detective Koo, I have the information you asked for," she said, not noticing the impatient
look in Ellie's eye.

Ellie was tempted to tell Wells to leave it on her desk, but sighed and said, "Well, let's take a   10
look."

They walked back to Ellie's desk. She turned her lamp on and made some space on her messy
desk. Wells told her whose fingerprints were found on the items stolen from the safe and in the pages
of Allison's diary.

"Wait a minute," Ellie said, frowning. "This doesn't make sense." She took out her notebook   15
and reviewed the information. Ideas were beginning to form; connections were coming clear. She

stared at her lamp, and thought, surprisingly, about her daughter Sofia. "Boys," she finally said, smiling.

"Excuse me?" Wells asked.

"Officer Wells, are you working late tonight?" 20

"Yes, ma'am," she said, standing up straight.

Ellie thought about the crime scene and gave Wells instructions. Then she walked out to her car almost certain that she knew who the criminal was.

The next morning, Ellie walked Sofia and Colleen to the elementary school where the summer camp was located. It was already hot outside, but Ellie still wore her black coat. Colleen ran off when 25 she saw the "mall boys." Sofia stayed behind for a moment.

"Thanks for letting me go to the mall, *mamá*," she said.

Ellie wanted to give Sofia a kiss on the forehead, but didn't want to embarrass her in front of her friends. "Actually, I should thank you. I think you helped me solve a case."

Sofia's eyes became huge. "I did? How?" 30

Now Ellie did kiss her on the forehead, unable to resist. "Tell you later."

About thirty minutes later, Ellie was at the police station, hoping that Wells had the proof she needed. Yokota was waiting for her at her desk.

"You kept poor Officer Wells busy last night," he said, handing her a folder.

Ellie set down her morning coffee and opened the folder. She read the information twice, and 35 then looked up at her friend. "Do you know what this means?"

"I think I do," Yokota confessed, "but maybe you could explain it to me anyway."

"Happily," she said, smiling widely. "First, are the Reed kids at the hospital?"

Yokota nodded. "They're there with Judith. Lucia is here, visiting her son."

"Perfect," she said. "Let's get to the hospital, then. If he's lucky, Miguel might be out of jail in a 40 few hours."

Room 4123 of Georgetown Hospital was crowded when Ellie and Yokota arrived. Allison Reed was sitting next to her mother, looking sad and serious as Nancy explained that she had to forget about Miguel and marry Derrick. Judith was standing next to her son, apologizing again and again for giving Miguel the combination to the safe. Kevin was sitting between the beds, playing with his cell phone. 45

"Feeling better?" Ellie asked, looking from Nancy to Evan. Nancy looked much better than the day before. Her hair was brushed, her face had some color in it, and she was sitting up straight in bed. Evan, however, looked the same.

"Much," Nancy said. "We're all surprised that Miguel would do this to our family, but happy   50
and grateful that he's behind bars."

Allison, staring down at the floor, didn't look happy or grateful.

"Were you surprised to learn that your daughter was dating the man who drugged you?" Ellie
asked.

"I couldn't believe it," Nancy exclaimed. "But then again, everyone makes mistakes. It's best if   55
we just put all of this behind us."

"You really had no idea that Allison and Miguel were dating?" Ellie never took her eyes off of
Nancy.

"Not until yesterday, when you told us."

"Not even after you read about it in Allison's diary?"   60

The room changed all at once. Nancy froze in place. Allison stood up in a flash, knocking her
chair backwards. Evan sat up in his bed. Judith took a step back, using the wall for support. Kevin was
the only one who spoke; he laughed and said, "You did what?"

Nancy's face finally unfroze, and she said calmly, "Detective, that is crazy. I would never do
that." Then, turning to Allison, she added, "Believe me, honey, I would never read your diary."   65

Ellie walked over to Allison and put a comforting hand on her shoulder. Behind her, Yokota
filled the doorway, making sure that no one entered or left.

"Mrs. Reed," Ellie said, "your fingerprints are all over your daughter's diary, especially on the
pages from this summer, about Miguel."

Allison twisted away from Ellie and ran to the other side of the room, to stand next to her   70
grandmother. Nancy called after her, "Honey, don't go. I found the diary when I was cleaning your
room. I'm sorry."

"You don't clean my room, mother," shouted Allison. "Lucia does."

Ellie said, "I can tell you when she read it, Allison. The last page she touched was dated nine
days ago." Turning to Evan, she asked, "Mr. Reed, wasn't it about a week ago that your wife told you   75
that she saw Miguel stealing Allison's watch? Isn't that when she told you that she wanted to kick
Miguel out of the house?"

Evan didn't have time to answer, because Allison cried out, "He didn't steal my watch! I gave
it to him. I gave it to him on the Georgetown campus. You couldn't have seen us, mother. Did you go
looking through his room, too?"   80

Kevin was the only Reed not staring at Nancy. He was still laughing. "I can't wait to text my
friends about this."

"You lied to me, Mrs. Reed," Ellie continued. "You told me that you didn't know that Miguel and Allison were dating. Why did you do that?"

Nancy looked apologetic for a moment, but then said angrily, "So I lied. I don't have to explain myself to you. Who cares if I lied?" 85

Ellie was standing at the foot of Nancy's bed. She bent to her knees so that her eyes were level with Nancy's. "I care. I care because you lied about a lot of things." Ellie slipped her notebook out of her pocket. She slowly flipped through the pages, and read from her point-form notes, "*Nancy Reed's statement: Lucia brought tea around 9:30 p.m. Too hot, so N. set it on the table and kept reading. E. got out* 90 *of the shower, N. went to bathroom, brushed hair. Then N. went back to bed and drank tea. Started to feel sick, set book on table, tried to go to bathroom. Felt too sick, so just lay there. Last thing she remembers.* Isn't that what you told me, Mrs. Reed?"

Nancy nodded silently, her eyes like guns pointed at Ellie. "Sounds right," she muttered.

"Then why was your lamp turned off when Lucia and Judith found you the next morning?" 95

"I... I guess I made a mistake," Nancy said slowly. Then with more confidence, she added, "I was drugged, detective. I'm sorry I can't remember every detail."

Ellie stood up straight and scratched below her ear. "You're right, Mrs. Reed, you were drugged. I apologize. But explain this. Why didn't your tea spill when you tried to get up and go to the bathroom?"

Nancy Reed started to speak, then stopped. She looked at her husband, then her mother-in-law, 100 then her daughter, and finally even her son. Nobody offered any suggestions. "I can't explain it," Nancy said. "Maybe it did spill."

"No," Judith said quickly. "When Lucia shook you in the morning, the tea was still in the cup. That's when it spilled."

Ellie turned to Judith and said, "Ms. Reed, last night I stood on Evan and Nancy's bed. Now I 105 can understand why you don't open the safe by yourself. The mattress is very soft, and the whole bed shakes when you walk." Turning back to Nancy, she added, "Mrs. Reed, why didn't your tea spill when Miguel climbed onto the bed, moved the painting, opened the safe, and took the items out? That seems odd to me."

"Who knows?" snapped Nancy. "All of this is very interesting, but none of it proves that I did 110 anything wrong. Are you accusing me of something?"

Ellie nodded, considering the information that Wells had discovered. "Mrs. Reed," she said to Nancy, "do I remember correctly that you last opened the safe about two weeks ago, when you and your husband took out some cash?"

Nancy hesitated, but then said, "That's right." 115

"We dusted the items from the safe. Your fingerprints are on almost all of the items."

"Of course," Nancy said confidently. "Of course *my* fingerprints are on the items in *my* safe."

Turning to Judith, Ellie said, "Ms. Reed, you opened the safe – or, rather, Miguel opened it for you – on Sunday, just five days ago, to put in the Inverted Eagle stamp. Is that right?"

Judith nodded.   120

"Then can someone explain to me," Ellie asked the group, "how Nancy Reed's fingerprints could be on the Inverted Eagle?"

Ellie let the silence hang in the air. She glanced at Yokota. He was doing his best not to smile as he guarded the doorway.

All eyes were on Nancy Reed, who finally said, "Actually, I made a mistake. I opened the safe a   125
couple of days ago, and I handled Judith's new stamp. I must have forgotten." It was such an obvious lie that Ellie almost laughed out loud.

"That's one possibility," Ellie said, backing away from Nancy, leaving her alone on her side of the room. Even Kevin was away from the window, standing next to his sister and squeezing her hand. "Let me give you another possibility. I think you read Allison's diary nine days ago. You couldn't believe what   130
you were reading. Allison was planning to break up with Derrick Quenton, the son of one of the richest men in America, because she wanted to date the son of the housekeeper. I can imagine how disappointed you must have been, especially considering your husband's financial ruin."

Judith, Allison, and Kevin Reed all gasped and looked at Evan, but he was so focused on his wife that he didn't even notice.   135

"You had to get Miguel out of the picture," Ellie continued, "but you knew from Allison's diary that she was deeply in love with him. You probably thought about it for a couple days. Then you noticed your husband's sleeping pills still in the kitchen. You realized that if you could frame Miguel for a crime, especially one that injured you and your husband, then Allison would have no choice but to break up with him."   140

Nancy opened her mouth to protest, but no words escaped.

Ellie turned to Judith and asked, "Ms. Reed, on the day you bought the Inverted Eagle, what time did you get home?"

"Pretty late," Judith said. "It was dark outside. The auction was in Maryland, near Baltimore. It took a long time to get home."   145

Ellie glanced in her notebook and said, "You told me that you were surprised that Nancy wasn't home when you arrived. Why was that?"

Judith thought it over, and answered, "Well, her car was in the driveway, first of all. Also, it was Lucia's day off, and Nancy usually cooks dinner on Sundays."

"But you couldn't find her, so you asked Miguel to put the stamp away, right?"   150

Judith nodded, then turned to Nancy suddenly. "You were home, weren't you? You saw Miguel and me go into the bedroom. You knew that he had the combination."

"No," Nancy said. She said it again, but could think of nothing else to say.

Ellie continued, "Ms. Reed, you told me that you and your son and your daughter-in-law like to sit alone in the dark library. In fact, last night you were sitting in the library, and I couldn't see you when I left Evan and Nancy's bedroom. I think that Nancy was sitting in the same chair Sunday evening, keeping quiet. I think that Nancy wanted you to give Miguel the combination. She knew that after the robbery, the police would discover that he knew it and suspect him of the crime. She didn't know that her own son also knew the combination." Ellie glanced at Kevin, who was staring at his mother and shaking his head

"The rest was easy," Ellie continued, looking again at Nancy. "One afternoon, alone in the house, or while Judith was busy, you took her keys. Then you took Allison's watch from Miguel's room. On that same day, Tuesday perhaps, or Wednesday morning, you took the items from the safe and hid them in Miguel's room. You didn't wear gloves when you took the items from the safe, since your fingerprints were already on all of the items, or so you thought. But you did remember to put gloves on when you opened the vent and hid the items inside. You knew that you had to act quickly because soon Judith or Evan would open the safe and notice that it was empty. You had your husband's sleeping pills crushed and ready to use. You must have been thrilled Wednesday night when you took a sip of your tea and noticed that there was no honey in it. Lucia never forgets your honey, but Miguel often does. The police would certainly discover, as I did, that Miguel prepared the tea. With Evan in the shower, you added the crushed sleeping pills to the tea. However, you didn't know that you were allergic to them. To think… you almost killed yourself, ruining your perfect plan."

All at once Nancy lost her temper. "You can't prove any of this! Okay, I forgot that I opened the safe and touched Judith's stamp. So what? You have no real evidence. A court would never find me guilty." Her voice was so ugly and full of anger that everyone in her family, even her husband, looked away from her.

"I was worried about that, too," Ellie said, opening Wells' file. "That's why I asked one of our officers to run some tests last night. You like to sleep in your socks, Mrs. Reed. I have the same habit. Anyway, when you were brought to the hospital, your clothing became evidence. Can you guess what we found on the bottom of your socks?" Ellie only waited a moment to answer her own question: "Dried tea, the same tea used to drug you and your husband. You waited until your husband was unconscious. Then you stood up and opened the safe to frame Miguel for the robbery. Your husband's tea was all over the bed, and you stepped right in it. Can you think of any other way that the tea could be on the bottom of your feet?"

Nancy Reed didn't answer Ellie's question, nor did she say another word as Yokota placed her under arrest. 185

Back at the police station, Ellie released Miguel and apologized. Then she wished him luck at Georgetown, and with Allison.

That afternoon, Ellie walked with Vi to the summer camp and picked Sofia up herself. She also talked to the boys who wanted to go to the mall, and their parents. 190

On the way home, Sofia jumped onto her mother's back and said, "Hey, you never told me how I helped you with your hot case."

Sofia had become too heavy for piggy-back rides. Ellie set her down on the sidewalk and said…

```
"  y  o  u      m  a  d  e      m  e      t  h  i  n  k
   4 17 15     13 10 19  1     13 14     20 18  2  5 12

   a  b  o  u  t      m  o  t  h  e  r  s ,
  10  6  7 15 20     13  7 20 18 14  3 11

   d  a  u  g  h  t  e  r  s ,     a  n  d      b  o  y  s .
  19 10 15  9 18 20  1 16 11     10  5 19      6 17  4 11

   s  o  m  e      m  o  t  h  e  r  s      w  o  r  r  y
  11  7 13 14     13  7 20 18  1 16 11      8 17  3 16  4

   m  o  r  e      t  h  a  n      I      d  o ."
  13 17  3 14     20 18 10  5      2     19 17
```

"That's impossible," Sofia said, trying again to jump on her mother's back. "You're the worst."

"No, it's true," Ellie insisted. "In my hot case, there was a mother who was so worried about her 195 daughter's boyfriend that she did something very foolish."

"Did anyone die?" Sofia asked, suddenly very quiet behind Ellie.

Ellie dropped to one knee. "Fortunately, no one died, but some people did get hurt." Ellie grabbed Sofia's hand and they waited for the *WALK* sign to cross Mt. Pleasant Street. "So, if I ever disapprove of one of your boyfriends, I'll just talk to you about it." 200

"Boyfriends?" cried Sofia, squeezing her mother's hand. "Yuck! Some boys are kind of cute, but I'll never have a boyfriend."

Ellie smiled, wishing that it were true.

END OF CHAPTER 6   END OF CHAPTER 6   END OF CHAPTER 6   END OF CHAPTER 6

Instructions:

To discover what Ellie said, answer the following vocabulary and comprehension questions. After you have answered all of the questions, use the letters of the correct responses and the circled letters to solve the puzzle on page 74.

A. Vocabulary Questions

1) "She learned Evan Reed had received several loans from Washington Bank, where he worked." (Line 2) If a bank gives you a loan, then you _____ the money, and the bank _____ the money to you.
   d) lend; borrows
   e) borrow; lends
   f) win, loses
   g) lose; wins

2) "It's best if we just put all of this behind us." (Line 56) Which one of the following would you *not* want to put behind you?
   g) a volleyball game that your team loses
   h) a disagreement with your friend
   i) a happy childhood memory
   j) a disappointing math test

   In other words, what does it mean to put something behind you?

   _____

3) "Nancy looked apologetic for a moment, but then said angrily..." (Line 85)

   If you are apologetic, then you feel

   ___ ___ (_)___ Y.

4) "The mattress is very soft, and the whole bed shakes when you walk." (Line 107) If something shakes, then it:
   w) makes a loud noise
   x) moves down; lowers
   y) moves from side to side
   z) moves up; raises

   How is shaking different than nodding?

   _____

5) "Mrs. Reed, why didn't your tea spill when Miguel climbed onto the bed, moved the painting, opened the safe, and took the items out? That seems odd to me." (Line 107)

   Another word for odd is:

   S _ _ _ _ (_)G _ .

6) "She glanced at Yokota. He was doing his best not to smile as he guarded the doorway." (Line 123) To glance is to:
   b) look quickly
   c) stare for a long time
   d) move your eyebrows up in surprise
   e) wave with your hands

7) "I opened the safe a couple of days ago, and I handled Judith's new stamp." (Line 126) A couple usually refers to which number or set of numbers?
   n) 1
   o) 2
   p) between 5 and 10
   q) more than 10

8) "Even Kevin was away from the window, standing next to his sister and squeezing her hand." (Line 129) If you squeeze something, then you:
   t) let it go
   u) move it up and down
   v) touch it lightly
   w) hold it tightly

9) "I can imagine how disappointed you must have been, especially considering your husband's financial ruin." (Line 133) The *opposite* of ruin is:
   d) future
   e) secret
   f) decline
   g) success

10) "Judith, Allison, and Kevin Reed all gasped and looked at Evan, but he was so focused on his wife that he didn't even notice." (Line 134) When a person gasps, he or she _____ because he or she is _____.
    y) breathes out; angry
    z) breathes out; surprised
    a) breathes in, surprised
    b) breathes in, angry

11) "Nancy opened her mouth to protest, but no words escaped." (Line 141) Which one of the following definitions of protest is correct in this sentence?
- s) disagree
- t) scream
- u) ask
- v) demonstrate

12) "Also, it was Lucia's day off, and Nancy usually cooks dinner on Sundays." (Line 149)

On someone's day off, he or she does not have

to: W _o_ _r_ _(_ _k_ _)_ .

B. Comprehension Questions

13) How does the author create suspense, or mystery, in the beginning of this chapter?
- j) by making Ellie and Yokota disagree about the crime
- k) by showing problems in Ellie's personal life
- l) by making the reader think that Kevin is guilty
- m) by not telling the reader what information Wells discovered

14) Ellie can prove that Nancy read Allison's diary because of Nancy's F _i_ _n_ _g_ _(_ _e_ _)_ _r_ -
___ ___ ___ ___ ___ ___ .

15) Which one of the following statements can we guess about Ellie?
- t) She probably doesn't trust Officer Wells.
- u) She probably tells Sofia about some of her cases.
- v) She probably yells at Sofia in front of other people.
- w) She probably has an organized filing system for her papers.

16) What does Judith realize before Ellie says it?
- p) that Nancy took her keys
- q) that Evan lost all of his money
- r) that Nancy saw her give the combination to Miguel
- s) that Nancy read Allison's diary

17) The most important evidence was discovered on

Nancy's _S_ _(_ _o_ _)_ _c_ _k_ _s_ .

18) In the beginning of the chapter, Wells shows Ellie some information. Ellie tells her, "This doesn't make sense." What was she talking about?
- h) Nancy's fingerprints on the Inverted Eagle
- i) Nancy's fingerprints in Allison's diary
- j) Nancy's fingerprints on the jewelry box
- k) Nancy's fingerprints on the safe

19) Ellie discovers that Nancy has lied about all of the following except:
- c) knowing about Allison and Miguel's relationship
- d) her financial situation
- e) seeing Miguel take Allison's watch
- f) when she last opened the safe

20) Ellie asks Wells, "Are you working late tonight?" because she still needs one more piece of information. What is it?
- q) She wants to know whose fingerprints are on the teacups.
- r) She wants to know if there was any honey in Evan's tea.
- s) She wants to know if it was really Kevin who made the tea.
- t) She wants to know if any tea spilled on Nancy's clothes.

Now, go back to page 74 and fill in the puzzle answers to find out what Ellie said.

CHAPTER REVIEW

A. Police Briefing

Get into small groups and select a chief detective. The chief detective will lead group discussions, and make sure all members are participating.

1. Check your Chapter 6 puzzle answers with your group.

2. Discuss the evidence and complete the box below.

What were the most important clues that finally broke the case?

Clue	Why was it important?
Fingerprints on the Inverted Eagle	

Chapter 6: The Arrest | 77

B. **Listen to the CD**

You will hear the criminal's confession. After you listen, answer the questions.

How did the criminal carry out the crime? List the most important events in the order that they happened

1. _____
2. _____
3. _____
4. _____
5. _____
6. _____
7. _____
8. _____
9. _____
10. _____

What was Ellie wrong about?

_____

What was the biggest mistake the criminal made? Discuss.

_____

C. Think Back

Discuss the following questions.

1. Could you guess who the criminal was? When did you know?
2. What most surprised you about this case?

D. Quiz

Complete the quiz. You may use your Detective's Notebook, but close this book.

Story 2
Death On U Street

by Adam Gray

Crime Talk

The following words and expressions will be important for understanding and talking about this story. Look for a list of Crime Talk words at the beginning of each chapter (for example, page 82). Those are the Crime Talk words that will appear in that chapter.

badge – a card or metal piece that identifies your job

blackmail –asking for money to keep a secret

CIA – Central Intelligence Agency, the organization in the United States government that seeks secret information about other countries

confess – say that you did a crime

coroner – a doctor who examines people who have died

dirty cop – a police officer who breaks the law

handcuffs – metal rings connected by a chain that can be locked; police use these to stop people from moving their hands freely

holding cell – a jail where suspects are kept after they are arrested

line of questioning – a series of connected questions about a topic

murderer – a person who kills another person not by mistake

outline – the shape of a victim's body made with tape or chalk

suspicion – a doubt about a person or case

suspicious – seeming strange or false

warrant – a piece of paper, signed by a judge, that allows the police to enter and search a building

weapon – an object used to hurt another person

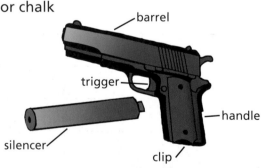

barrel

trigger

handle

silencer

clip

What word or expression is shown by each picture? Write it in the space.

'Give me $ 100000 r I will tell the police

_____

_____

_____

Chapter 1 : **Pre-reading**

This story is about a murder. In this chapter, Ellie learns about the victim and about the situation surrounding the crime. She also meets some possible suspects.

• **Answer these pre-reading questions alone or with a partner. If you don't know the answer, guess.**

1. What are some reasons someone might murder another person? Think about recent cases in the news.

   _____

   _____

   _____

   _____

   _____

2. What facts do you think Ellie needs to know right away? What questions should she ask? The first example is done for you.

   What is the crime? _____

   _____

   _____

   _____

   _____

   _____

Chapter 1

The Victim

Crime Talk: case, confess, coroner, dirty cop, evidence, robbery, suspect, victim

Detective Eliana Koo turned onto U Street and saw lights. The biggest light was the sun   1
peeking between the buildings in the Adams Morgan neighborhood of Washington DC. The other
lights were less friendly. They were the flashing of four police cars and an ambulance parked near the
corner of 7th Street. She parked and took a few sips of her morning coffee.

"Here we go," she whispered to herself. Moments later she was ducking under the yellow police   5
tape.

"Good morning, Detective Koo," called a voice she knew.

"I don't know if it's good," she replied, "but it's very cold." In truth, the weather wasn't too bad
for the middle of December, but it was too cold for Ellie.

Officer Kazuo Yokota, one of her best friends on the police force, gave her a quick handshake.   10
"I don't mind the cold," he said. "Neither does our victim."

"What's the situation?" she asked, removing her detective's notebook from her pocket.

"One victim, male, single gunshot wound to the chest," Yokota answered quickly. "A pedestrian
saw him through the window about twenty minutes ago and called 9-1-1." Yokota was pointing to the
front window of Eagle Eye Pawn Shop. Eagle Eye was one of the best pawn shops in the city. Like all   15

pawn shops, it bought and sold used objects, but Eagle Eye was known for having high-quality jewelry and art.

"Do we know who he is?" Ellie asked, entering the store in front of Yokota. She noticed that there were thick metal bars over all of the windows.

"Terrance Sweet," Yokota called behind her. "His driver's license was in his wallet. African-American, 37 years old. It looks like he was a security guard. He is wearing a uniform and had a gun under his jacket."

Eagle Eye was a large and very crowded store. Ellie weaved through several aisles of TVs, telephones, lamps, boots, stereos, statues, cameras, and countless knick-knacks. "Who owns this store?" she asked.

She heard Yokota flipping through his own notebook. "Leo Mench, 52 years old. Divorced, one son named Noah. Lives not far from here, over on P Street."

"Send a car to pick him up. I'd like to talk to him."

Ellie heard Yokota talk into his police radio. She took one more turn and found the scene of the crime. In the back of the store was an open vault. In front of the vault, almost inside of it, was the body of Terrance Sweet.

"I know him!" Ellie called out suddenly. All of the police officers stopped what they were doing and looked at her. "Terry Sweet. He used to be a police officer. He left the police force about six or seven years ago." Ellie knew more, but didn't say anything else out loud. She knew that Sweet had been a dirty cop. They caught him taking money and valuables from crime scenes. That was the reason he lost his job as a police officer.

"We found these in his pockets, ma'am," said a female officer, pointing to a small pile of items on the floor. The two women smiled at each other. Ellie knew Natalie Wells from a case they worked together over the summer. Five months after that case, Wells seemed much more confident and relaxed.

Ellie put on a pair of gloves. Sweet's wallet had over $100 in it and two credit cards. She picked up his gun. It was cold, and the bullet chamber was full. She set it down and picked up a key chain.

"Officer Yokota," she said, "please check to see if one of these keys opens the front door."

Returning to the pile, she found a black cell phone and a folded piece of paper. She opened the paper and mumbled, "'16-33-28.' What in the world is this?" But she knew the answer right away. "Officer Wells, please check to see if the combination to the vault is 16-33-28."

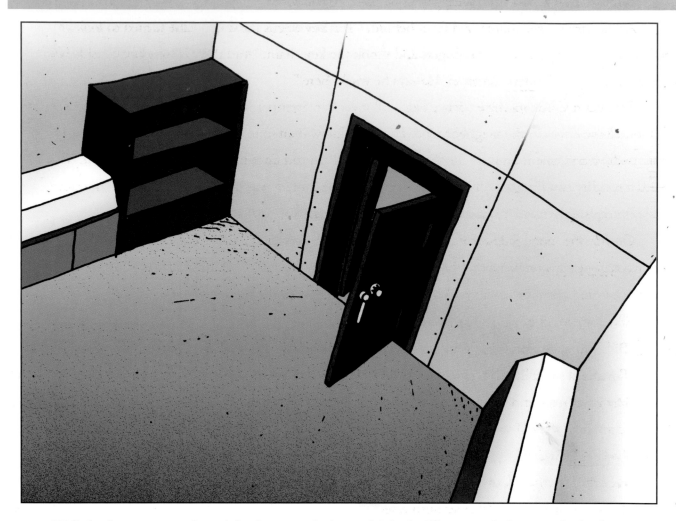

Wells had to step over Sweet's body to reach the vault's lock. Ellie moved closer to the body as well. She touched Sweet's arm. It was cold. Ellie figured that he'd been dead for several hours, but the coroner would be able to tell her for sure. Sweet was tall, muscular, and handsome, and wore a short, clean beard. The bullet wound was near his heart. The blood on his clothes was already dry.   50

Ellie stood up and examined the scene more closely. It looked like Sweet was shot right outside the vault, facing the front of the pawn shop. His arms were spread outward from his body and his hands were open and clean, which was unusual. Ellie knew that victims who are shot this way are usually found with blood on their hands, from touching their wound.

Also, if he had a gun, Ellie wondered, *why didn't he reach for it?* She wrote down those questions   55
and several more. Why was he inside the store? Why did he open the vault? Who gave him the combination?

"And what is this?" she asked out loud. She bent over the body and picked up a small piece of wood. Looking closely, she saw that there were more wood fragments. Some were on his chest and others were on the floor. She slipped some of the fragments into an evidence bag.   60

"You were right, ma'am," Wells said. "16-33-28 is the code."

At the same time, Yokota said from behind, "This key opens the door." Ellie turned to look at him. He held the longest key in his fingers and shook the key chain. "And there is someone outside who wants to talk to you. William Stemper. He says he works here."

Ellie handed Yokota the evidence bag. "I'll meet Mr. Stemper in front of the shop. Have officers knock on all the doors in the neighborhood. I want to know if anyone saw or heard anything strange." Yokota nodded agreement and left the shop. Ellie looked around once more before following him. She noticed a security camera above her head. Surprisingly, the camera was not facing the front of the store or the cash register. Instead it was looking straight down, and was turned off.

Outside the shop, the morning was brighter and the crowd was larger. One man in his thirties, wearing a heavy coat over pajamas, was waving at Ellie. A Washington Redskins hat was pulled over his ears. Ellie nodded at a police officer who then let the man pass under the yellow tape.

Ellie slipped off her gloves and offered a hand. "William Stemper?"

"Billy," he said, nodding. "Call me Billy. Is it true that Terry is dead?"

"I'm afraid so," Ellie said, trying to read Billy's face. "You work here?"

Billy breathed out deeply. He was shaking, probably from the cold. "Yes, with Mr. Mench. And I live right down the street. I saw the police cars when I woke up and ran straight here."

"And Terry Sweet?"

"He's the security guard. He works for all three businesses."

Ellie shook her head. "All *three* businesses?"

"Yeah," Billy said. "Eagle Eye, U Street Camera, and the Cane Gallery."

Now Ellie understood. Eagle Eye Pawn Shop was on the corner of U Street and 7th. Next door to Eagle Eye was the camera shop, U Street Camera. Next to the camera shop was the Cane Art Gallery. It was well-known, but Ellie could not remember why.

"Why have I heard of the Cane Gallery?" she asked.

"Probably because of the artist, Ross Curran."

Billy was right. She remembered reading about the Cane Gallery in the Washington Post. Ross Curran was a local artist who was becoming very popular. He was a friend of the owner of the Cane Gallery and sold all of his paintings there. Thanks to Curran, the gallery was becoming very popular as well.

"So Sweet worked as the security guard for all three stores?" she confirmed.

"Right, for about six months. But I knew him before that. He used to work at U Street Camera. His brother-in-law, Roland Walker, is the owner."

That seemed interesting to Ellie. "Roland is married to Terry's sister?"

"No, Roland isn't married. Terry is married to Roland's sister, Sara." Billy paused and looked 95

down. "*Was* married, I guess."

"And who is the owner of the Cane Gallery?" Ellie asked.

"Ling Cane. She's from Singapore, but her husband is American. Nice guy, kind of boring."

Billy kept on mumbling, giving Ellie a chance to take some notes.

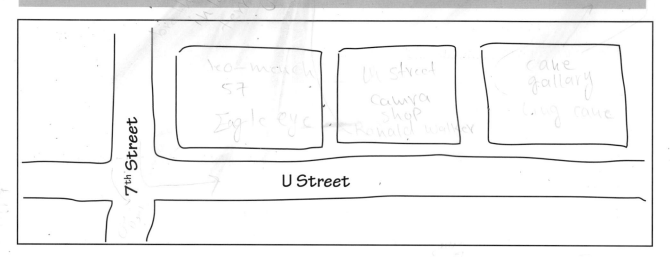

Map It: Complete this map by labeling the three businesses in the boxes below. Include the names of the owners.

"I wanted to ask about the video camera in the shop," Ellie interrupted. "Why is it turned off?" 100

"It's broken," Billy said. "Terry was fixing it. Bad luck, huh? The camera breaks two days

before…" He didn't finish his sentence.

Ellie didn't believe in luck, good or bad. Quickly she asked, "Do you know the combination to

the vault?"

"No way," he said, waving his hands. "Only Mr. Mench knows the combination." 105

"So Terry didn't know?"

"Are you kidding? He didn't even have a copy of the key! He only came into the store to work on

the video camera. Other than that, he worked outside, and only after the store was closed."

Ellie nodded. "But you have a key?"

"Yes," Billy said quickly. Then he added: "Why?" 110

"Can I see it?"

Billy hesitated, but pulled his keys from his coat pocket. Ellie asked Yokota to check the door

with Billy's key.

They waited in silence for a moment. Billy played with the buttons of his coat.

"Did you like Terry?" Ellie asked. 115

"Sure, he was all right."

"Um-hm. Did anyone dislike him?"

"Dislike him? You mean, would somebody want to hurt him? I don't know. I mean, I don't think so."

Ellie tried to make eye contact with Billy, but he was studying the sidewalk again. "You live alone, Billy?"

Now Billy looked right at her. "Am I a suspect? I liked Terry, really!"

"These are just standard questions. So you were alone last night?"

Billy nodded.

"Did you hear or see anything strange?"

He shook his head regretfully.

Yokota returned the keys to Ellie, shaking his head, too.

"Mr. Stemper, you *don't* have a key to the store. However, we found a key in Mr. Sweet's pocket."

Billy looked confused. "You mean Terry stole my key?"

"I don't know. Could he have switched the two keys? The fake key for the real key?"

Billy looked thoughtful. "Well, he did borrow my keys the other day. He wanted to test the lock."

"Have you used your key since then?"

"No, I almost never use my key. Mr. Mench opens and closes the store."

Ellie asked Billy a few more questions and then sent him to Officer Wells. In her mind, Billy was definitely a suspect. He lived nearby, the victim had his key, and Ellie sensed that he was hiding something.

Behind Ellie, the paramedics were taking Sweet's body out of the shop. Cameras were clicking, but the body was covered. Ellie felt a cold morning chill. She stepped back inside the shop and was soon studying the open vault.

The vault was about six feet deep by six feet wide. Ellie took one step inside, but then heard, "Are you in charge here? That is my personal property. Please do not go in there."

Ellie stepped back. She studied the short, stocky man who was walking her way. Yokota was two steps behind him, asking him to stop. Ellie waved her hand at Yokota, telling him that it was all right. "I'm Detective Koo," she said firmly, standing up straight. "You must be Mr. Mench."

Mench stopped in front of Ellie. Then he looked down and saw blood on the floor. The anger left his face. "Oh my God," he whispered. "Poor Terry. What happened?"

"That's what I want to find out," she said, guiding Mench away from the vault.

Ellie asked Mench about Sweet and about the pawn shop. He confirmed everything that Billy told her.

"We hired Terry after the robbery, about six months ago."

"The robbery?" Ellie asked.

"First, someone broke the windows of the Cane Gallery. Then, about a week later, someone   155
broke into the camera shop. Ling, Roland, and I agreed that we needed some security. Roland
recommended his brother-in-law, Terry."

Ellie finished taking her notes. Then she looked Mench in the eye. "I need to look at your vault
now. Are you coming?"

Leo Mench hesitated, but then nodded. Ellie wondered what secrets he had inside the vault. She   160
handed Mench a pair of gloves.

"Why do you have a vault, Mr. Mench?"

"Oh, I bought it years ago. It's perfect for storing my most valuable items. It's fireproof, so I keep
my papers there, too."

Inside, Ellie watched Mench very carefully. He opened and closed jewelry cases. He counted   165
rings, watches, bracelets, and earrings. There were several expensive-looking cameras. Against the far wall
was a leaning stack of paintings. Mench counted and checked them. Ellie admired the painting on top.

"That's a Ross Curran, right?" Ellie asked. She recognized the thick, snake-like swirls that were in
most of Curran's work.

Mench smiled for the first time. "That's right."   170

It was a beautiful gray, red and yellow painting with six silver swirls of different sizes. Its
beautiful wood frame had the same swirls etched in it. "You bought it from the Cane Gallery?"

"No, actually," he said, still smiling. "Ling has a second gallery, in Singapore. Her brother runs it. I went to Singapore on vacation a few weeks ago and visited the gallery. The Currans are much cheaper over there. I'm going to ask Mr. Curran to write me a personal note on the back of the   175 painting." The smile left Mench's face. "But I guess that isn't important right now."

He continued to inspect the vault. He opened and closed several file cabinets. Then he did it. Ellie saw him. She saw him take a small, folded piece of paper and put it in his pocket. He did it quickly, but she saw. She didn't say anything. She waited to see what else he would do.

Finally Mench shook his head, turned to Ellie, and said…   180

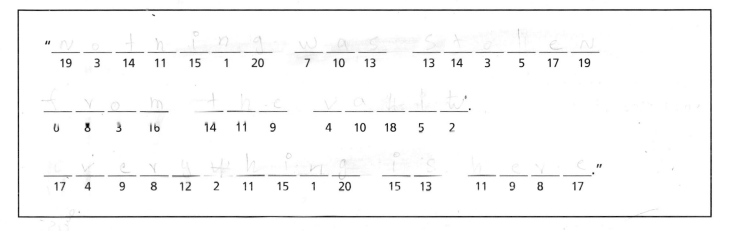

"Nothing at all?" Ellie asked. She looked down at Mench's pocket. She felt both anger and curiosity. "How can you be so sure?"

"Detective," Mench said very seriously, "I know everything that is in my vault. I know every ring, every document, every painting. I'm telling you that nothing was stolen."

Ellie nodded very slowly. "Well, Mr. Mench, we both know that something was stolen from the   185 vault. We also know who stole it." She paused and waited for Mench to confess. He did not. "Take the paper out of your pocket, Mr. Mench," she said coldly, "or I will arrest you right here, right now."

Mench closed his eyes and took a deep breath. Then he put the folded piece of paper into Ellie's open hand.

END OF CHAPTER 1

CHAPTER 1: PUZZLE

Instructions:

To discover what Mench said, answer the following vocabulary and comprehension questions. After you have answered all of the questions, use the letters of the correct responses and the circled letters to solve the puzzle on page 89.

A. Vocabulary Questions

1) "A pedestrian saw him through the window about twenty minutes ago and called 9-1-1." (Line 14)

   A <u>pedestrian</u> is a person who is

   W __a__ __l__ __k__ __i__ (__n__)__g__ along the street.

2) "Like all pawn shops, it bought and sold used objects, but Eagle Eye was known for having high-quality jewelry and art." (Line 16) You could find all of the following items in a <u>pawn shop</u> except:
   - t) a new car
   - u) an expensive watch
   - v) a diamond ring
   - w) a rare stamp

3) "It looks like he was a security guard. He is wearing a uniform and had a gun under his jacket." (Line 21)

   The job of a <u>security guard</u> is to

   P __r__ (__o__)__t__ __e__ __c__ __t__ a business or home.

4) "Ellie weaved through several aisles of TVs, telephones, lamps, boots, stereos, statues, cameras, and countless knick-knacks." (Line 23) If you <u>weave</u> from *Point A* to *Point B*, then you:
   - t) move in a straight line until you get to *Point B*
   - u) go to *Point B* as quickly as possible and then return to *Point A*
   - v) make many turns and twists as you walk to *Point B*
   - w) walk as slowly as possible, stopping to rest many times, on the way to *Point B*

5) "Ellie weaved through several aisles of TVs, telephones, lamps, boots, stereos, statues, cameras, and countless knick-knacks." (Line 23) All of the following places have <u>aisles</u> except:
   - l) a soccer field
   - m) a supermarket
   - n) an airplane
   - o) a movie theater

   What are aisles?

   _____

6) "Officer Wells, please check to see if the combination to the vault is 16-33-28." (Line 46) A <u>vault</u> is like a large:
   - c) desk
   - d) store
   - e) bank
   - f) safe

7) "Looking closely, she saw that there were more wood fragments." (Line 60) Which word is similar to <u>fragment</u>?
   - v) floor
   - w) piece
   - x) evidence
   - y) chest

8) "He was a friend of the owner of the Cane Gallery and sold all of his paintings there." (Line 89)

   A <u>gallery</u> is a place where you can buy or enjoy

   __A__ (__r__)__t__ .

9) "Could he have switched the two keys? The fake key for the real key?" (Line 129) If you <u>switch</u> two items, then you:
   - c) lose one of the items but not the other
   - d) steal both items
   - e) exchange the places where the items should be
   - f) change the names of the items

10) "Could he have switched the two keys? The fake key for the real key?" (Line 129) Another word for <u>fake</u> is:
   - y) old
   - z) broken
   - a) false
   - b) real

11) "She recognized the thick, snake-like swirls that were in most of Curran's work." (Line 168) Which one of these pictures could be a snake-like swirl?

h) ◎◎◎
i) ⣿
j) ⧕
k) ◎

12) "Its beautiful wood frame had the same swirls etched in it." (Line 172) It is common to buy a frame for a:
   t) computer
   w) radio
   x) book
   y) photograph

What is the purpose of a frame?

_____

B. Comprehension Questions

13) How did the police find out about the shooting of Terry Sweet?
   r) Terry Sweet was Ellie's friend.
   s) A pedestrian called 9-1-1.
   t) A police officer heard the gun shot.
   u) Billy Stemper found the body inside the pawn shop and ran to the police station.

14) Roland Walker is the owner of U Street Camera.

He is also Terry Sweet's

b r o (t) h e r -
i n - l a w .

15) Which one of the following statements can we guess about Ellie?
   g) She is trying to drink less coffee.
   h) She does not like to work with Officer Yokota.
   i) She likes the summer more than the winter.
   j) She is not interested in art.

16) Ellie noticed that the pawn shop's video camera was:
   l) pointed at the front door
   m) turned off
   n) hidden behind the cash register
   o) new

17) Ellie sees Leo Mench take a piece of

_ p _ a p (e) _ v _
from the vault.

18) All of these details about Terry Sweet's body are true except:
   r) that his arms are spread out on the floor
   s) that he is covered in small wood fragments
   t) that he is lying near the door of the vault
   u) that he has a gun in his right hand

19) How did Terry Sweet lose his job as a police officer?
   l) He made too many mistakes.
   m) He couldn't use his gun well.
   n) He stole from crime scenes.
   o) He was mean to suspects.

20) Leo Mench bought a Ross Curran painting in

S _ n _ (g) a p o r _ .

Now, go back to page 89 and fill in the puzzle answers to find out what Mench said.

A. Police Briefing

Get into small groups and select a chief detective. The chief detective will lead group discussions, and make sure all members are participating.

1. Check your Chapter 1 puzzle answers with your group.

2. Discuss the evidence and complete the box below.

What do we know about the victim, Terry Sweet?

Victim's name	Known facts
Terry Sweet	Married, no kids

B. **Listen to the CD**

TRACK 7

You will hear the call to 9-1-1 made by Cynthia, a bystander. After you listen, answer the questions.

1. Why did Cynthia look inside the pawn shop window?

_____

2. Why did Cynthia apologize to the 9-1-1 operator?

_____

3. Did Cynthia act bravely or cowardly? What would you have done? Discuss.

_____

C. Think Ahead

At the end of Chapter 1, Leo Mench tried to hide a piece of paper from Ellie. However, she was paying attention and saw him take it. What might be on the paper? Make a list of three possibilities.

1. _____

2. _____

3. _____

D. Quiz

Complete the quiz. You may use your Detective's Notebook, but close this book.

Chapter 2 : Pre-reading

Previously in *Whodunit... The Victim*

The following panels show three important events from Chapter 1. Order and caption each panel.

Chapter 2 : Blackmail

In this chapter, Ellie learns some suspicious facts about the victim's boss, Leo Mench. She must also tell the bad news to Sara Sweet, the wife of the victim, and interview her charming brother, Roland.

• **Answer these pre-reading questions alone or with a partner. If you don't know the answer, guess.**

1. At the end of the last chapter, Leo Mench took a piece of paper from his vault. What do you think the paper could be?

   _____

   _____

2. Ellie goes to Sara Sweet's house in this chapter. Why could that be difficult for Ellie?

   _____

   _____

3. How is the crime in *Death on U Street* different than the crime in *The Inverted Eagle*?

   _____

   _____

   _____

Chapter 2

Blackmail

Ellie walked Mench out of the vault. Then she held up the small piece of paper, but looked at   1
Mench before she read it.

"Mr. Mench, tell me the truth before I read this. Was anything stolen from your vault?"

"I swear that nothing was stolen," Mench insisted. "Everything is still in there."

Ellie wasn't sure if she believed him. She turned her attention to the paper. It was a regular   5
piece of white printer paper. It was folded three times. Inside, the message was written in black ink in
all capital letters. It read:

> I HOPE YOU ENJOY THESE PHOTOS, MR. MENCH. I KNOW YOUR
> SECRET. I WILL STAY QUIET FOR THE RIGHT PRICE. I WANT
> $10,000 IN A SUITCASE. LEAVE THE SUITCASE IN THE GARBAGE
> CAN BEHIND YOUR STORE AT 8 P.M. ON THURSDAY. THEN GO HOME.
> DO NOT GO TO THE POLICE. I AM WATCHING YOU.

Ellie read the blackmail letter again. "Someone was blackmailing you, Mr. Mench. Why? What is this secret?"

"None of your business," he mumbled. "I don't have to tell you anything." 10

She tried another line of questioning. "The letter mentions photos."

"I burned them," Mench said, looking down at the floor. "I should have burned this letter, too."

"Why didn't you?"

"I don't know," he muttered. "I guess I thought it might be important later."

"Did you pay the blackmailer?" Ellie asked. When Mench didn't answer, she asked again. 15

"Yes, I paid, okay? Last Thursday I put the ten thousand dollars in a purple suitcase and left it in the garbage can. The next day it was gone. Okay? Are you satisfied?"

Ellie thought that Mench was probably angry for many reasons. Angry with himself for not burning the letter. Angry with Ellie for finding the letter. Angry with the blackmailer. Angry about losing the money. 20

Ellie looked at the date on her cell phone. It was Wednesday, December 17th. The blackmail was paid on Thursday, December 11th. "When did you receive the blackmail letter, Mr. Mench?"

He sighed and thought for a moment. "The week before. On Friday, I guess. It was in my mailbox at home."

"Did you receive other letters?" Ellie asked. 25

"No, just the one. I wasn't... I didn't..." Mench went silent.

"Yes, Mr. Mench?"

"I'm not saying anything else. I want my lawyer."

He was staring Ellie in the eye, but his body was trembling. She decided to try a friendly line of questioning. "Any information you give us will help us find Terry's murderer." 30

Nothing.

"Tell me why you were being blackmailed. You'll feel better."

Nothing.

"Do you know who was blackmailing you?"

"No," Mench said quickly. "I don't know who. Now I'm really not saying anything else." 35

Ellie asked more questions, but Mench didn't talk. Then she stopped being nice. "Leo Mench, you are under arrest for stealing evidence from a crime scene." She finished reading Mench his rights, then asked Yokota to put handcuffs on him. Mench looked terrified, but still did not speak. Finally Ellie said, "Take him to the station."

40

Outside, Ellie watched Yokota's police car drive away with Mench in the back seat. Officer Wells handed Ellie a cup of coffee. It was cold, but Ellie thanked her.

"Do you think he did it?" Wells asked.

"The murder?" Ellie asked. "I don't know. What do you think?"

"Well," started Wells, "he has a secret. It must be serious, because he paid ten thousand dollars   45
to cover it up. Maybe Sweet also knew the secret. Maybe Sweet was the blackmailer. Maybe it has nothing to do with Sweet's murder." Wells frowned. "I guess it's too early to say."

Ellie nodded and drank her coffee to be polite. "Do you have Sweet's address?"

"Yes, ma'am."

"Want to go for a ride?" Ellie asked.   50

Ellie was not looking forward to delivering the bad news to Sara Sweet. It was the worst part of the job. The Sweets lived in Arlington, Virginia, across the Potomac River. Ellie and Wells arrived in about twenty minutes. To her surprise, a man was sitting in a chair on the front porch of the suburban home. A good-looking man. A very good-looking man wearing blue jeans, a gray sweater, and a green winter coat.   55

"We've been waiting for you," he said as Ellie and Wells got out of the car. "We already know."

"And who are you?" Ellie asked.

"Roland Walker, Sara's brother. I also own the camera shop next to Eagle Eye Pawn Shop." Walker stood up to shake Ellie's hand. He was tall with short hair and a clean-shaven face. His dark eyes softened as Ellie introduced herself and Officer Wells.   60

"What is it that you know?" Ellie asked, putting her hands back into her coat pockets. "More importantly, how do you know it?"

"We know that Terry's dead. We know he was killed some time last night. Billy Stemper called Sara about forty-five minutes ago. She was in the shower, but he left a message. When she heard the message she called him back and then she called me. I live just a few minutes from here." As he spoke,   65
Roland Walker opened the front door and guided Ellie and Wells into the living room.

"Mr. Stemper should not have called you," Ellie said. She was annoyed with Stemper, but really this was her fault. It was her job to tell Sara Sweet about her husband. She had failed, and now she felt awful. "Is your sister all right?"

"She's upset, of course," Walker said, closing the door. "She's upstairs. I'll get her."   70

Ellie noticed a large green suitcase at the foot of the stairs. "Is Sara taking a trip?"

Roland let out a small smile. It was an attractive smile. Ellie tried to ignore it. "That's my suitcase. I threw some clothes in there before I came over. I'll be staying here for a few days, or as long as Sara needs me."

Walker disappeared upstairs. Ellie glanced around the living room. Then she noticed that Wells was staring at her.

"Yes, Officer Wells?" she asked.

"Nothing."

"Nothing?"

Natalie Wells stepped closer and whispered, "He isn't wearing a wedding ring, ma'am."

"Let's focus on the case," Ellie whispered coolly, trying to sound businesslike.

Moments later Walker returned, followed by his sister. Sara was tall and good-looking like her brother. She was still in her bathrobe. Dried tears stained her cheeks, but she was calm.

Ellie told Sara what she already knew. Then she apologized for not being the first person to tell her.

"It's all right," Sara said. They were seated on opposite sofas. "It's not your fault. Billy is like that. He… talks too much."

Roland returned from the kitchen with three cups of coffee. At the same time there was a knock on the door. Four uniformed officers were ready to search the house.

"Mrs. Sweet," Ellie said softly, "these officers are going to search the house. Is that all right?"

Sara looked at her brother. When he nodded, she nodded.

Ellie told the officers to begin upstairs and returned to the sofa. "And I need to ask you some questions. Is that okay?"

Sara nodded again, so Ellie began. She learned that Sara and Terry were married for eight years. They had no children. Sara was a legal secretary with a law firm in Arlington. She and Terry did not see each other very often because he worked nights. She last talked to Terry at about 6:00 p.m. the night before, before he left for work.

Sara Sweet was upset, but not as sad as Ellie would have thought. Ellie asked, "Mrs. Sweet, were you and Terry having any… marital problems?"

Sara sighed and took a sip of coffee. Again she looked at Roland.

"Tell them everything," Roland urged her.

"Well," she started, "it was a happy marriage in the beginning. I guess all marriages are happy in the beginning." Ellie nodded, thinking about her own marriage. "Things started to go bad when Terry lost his job. Did you know that Terry was a police officer?"

"Yes. I remember how he lost his job," Ellie said gently.

"Then you can imagine that it was very difficult. Terry was angry and depressed. He told me that he was innocent. I wasn't sure what to believe. He treated me well, so I supported him. He found jobs here and there for a couple of years, but nothing that he liked." She grabbed her brother's hand. "Then Roland was nice enough to give him a job at the camera shop, even though Terry knew nothing about cameras."

"How did that work out, Mr. Walker?" Ellie asked, looking down into her notebook.

"You can call me Roland," he answered. "It worked out well for a while. Terry did not care much about the business, but he tried. In the end, I had to let him go. I didn't want to. I just couldn't afford to keep him. Also, he wanted to try to get a job in security."

Ellie turned to Sara. "You were telling me about your marriage."

"Right. Well, the truth is that we were having problems. He changed, detective. He wasn't the same person I married. He started to drink more and more. He yelled sometimes." She was already speaking quietly, but added in a whisper: "And hit."

Ellie looked at Roland, to see his reaction. His face was calm, but there was anger in his eyes. The room was quiet. Ellie could hear the officers searching upstairs.

Sara continued. "Then he finally got a job in security, thanks to Roland. I thought he would be happy, but he was not. He complained all the time. And I think... well, Roland thinks..." She trailed off, again squeezing her brother's hand.

"Yes?" Ellie asked.

Roland spoke for his sister. "I think he was having an affair. I heard him talking on his cell phone many times outside the camera shop, when he was working. It sounded to me like he was talking to a woman. I told Sara, but she asked me not to say anything to him."

"Mrs. Sweet, do you think he was having an affair?"

She shook her head. "I don't know what to think. It's possible. We were not happy at home. We never saw each other, and he was cold to me. It's possible. I work all day and he was home alone."

Ellie asked a few more standard questions. She discovered that both Roland and Sara were alone when the crime was committed but that neither owned a gun. Neither Roland nor Sara could think of anyone who might want to hurt Terry.

Officer Wells had stayed quiet during the questioning. Now she asked, "Mrs. Sweet, is there anything else that we should know?"

Sara closed her eyes and seemed to think about the question. Tears started to run down her cheeks.

"What is it?" Roland asked, wiping her tears with his thumbs.

"There is one more thing," Sara said, standing up suddenly. She walked over to the front window and played with the curtains for a moment. Then she turned to the three curious people sitting on the sofas. "Terry said something very odd about two weeks ago. Not last Thursday, but the Thursday before. He was drinking here in the house. I asked him a question about money and he started laughing. Then he said, 'Money is not a problem for me, baby.' I asked him what he was talking about. He said, 'One of my bosses is going to give me a big Christmas bonus, and I mean a *big* one.' I didn't understand, because he doesn't get a Christmas bonus." 145

Ellie looked at Roland. He seemed surprised by Sara's story.

"Mrs. Sweet," she asked, "what did you think he meant?"

"I wasn't sure, but it sounded like he was talking about blackmail. I got the feeling that he was blackmailing one of his bosses—Roland, Ling, or Leo Mench." Ellie stole a glance at Wells. Her mouth was hanging open. Ellie was sure that they were both thinking about Mench's blackmail letter. 150

"Why didn't you say anything to me?" Roland asked.

"I don't know," she said, starting to cry again. "I figured that it was nothing, just Terry talking big."

Ellie turned to Roland Walker. "Do you know anything about this?"

"I have no idea what Terry was talking about," Roland said. "He was not blackmailing me, that's for sure. And I certainly wasn't going to give him a Christmas bonus." 155

Sara added, "Terry said one other odd thing that night. He said, 'After my bonus, the three of us are going to have a nice, long talk.' He was very angry."

"The *three* of you?" Ellie asked. "Who else was he talking about?"

"I have no idea," Sara said, shaking her head.

Chain of events: Write these important events from the story in the correct date boxes below: a) Terry Sweet was murdered b) Leo Mench paid the blackmailer c) Leo Mench received the blackmail letter d) Terry told Sara about the Christmas bonus e) The security camera broke (see Chapter 1).

SUNDAY	MONDAY	TUESDAY	WEDNESDAY	THURSDAY	FRIDAY	SATURDAY
	1	2	3	4	5	6
7	8	9	10	11	12	13
14	15	16	17	18	19	20

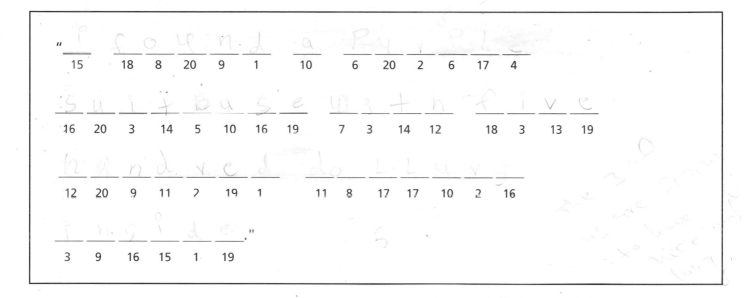

At that moment, one of the officers appeared at the top of the stairs. "Detective Koo, can I see you for a moment?"

Ellie excused herself and jogged up the stairs. She noticed a few pictures of Terry and Sara on the walls. They looked happy in the pictures, but the pictures all looked pretty old. The top of the stairs opened into a wide hallway.

"In here," the officer said, pointing to a door at the end of the hall. "We found it in the closet, under a box of heavy books."

"Found what?" Ellie asked. But then she turned the corner and saw it herself.

The officer continued…

160

165

Ellie stared at it for a few moments. Then she asked the officer to bring Sara and Roland upstairs. Ellie met them at the top of the stairs and pointed to the bedroom.

"Is that a guest bedroom?" Ellie asked.

"Yes," Sara answered, looking confused. "Roland is going to sleep there."

"But I haven't gone inside yet," Roland added quickly.

Together they walked to the doorway. "Do you recognize this?" Ellie asked, pointing to the purple suitcase, which was now closed.

Sara shook her head. "I've never seen that suitcase before. Whose is it?"

"I'm not sure," Ellie said. She was lying. She knew whose suitcase it was. So did Natalie Wells, who was looking at Ellie and slowly nodding her head.

170

175

Instructions:

To discover what the police officer said, answer the following vocabulary and comprehension questions. After you have answered all of the questions, use the letters of the correct responses and the circled letters to solve the puzzle on page 101.

A. Vocabulary Questions

1) "It must be serious, because he paid ten thousand dollars to cover it up." (Line 46)

   If you want to <u>cover up</u> something, then you

   want to H _i_ (_d_) _e_ it.

2) "Ellie was not looking forward to delivering the bad news to Sara Sweet." (Line 51)
   Most people <u>look forward to</u> all of the following *except*:
   - q) vacations
   - r) dentist appointments
   - s) parties and holidays
   - t) delicious meals

   What does it mean to look forward to something?

   _____

3) "To her surprise, a man was sitting in a chair on the front porch of the suburban home." (Line 53) A <u>suburban</u> home is always located:
   - i) outside of but near a city
   - j) in a poor area
   - k) in an old neighborhood
   - l) in the country; in a rural area

4) "It was her job to tell Sara Sweet about her husband. She had failed, and now she felt awful." (Line 69)

   To <u>feel awful</u> means to feel *bad*, or

   T _____ (_r_).

5) "Dried tears stained her cheeks, but she was calm." (Line 83) To <u>stain</u> a surface means to make the surface:
   - z) brighter
   - a) dangerous
   - b) unhappy
   - c) dirty

6) "Mrs. Sweet, were you and Terry having any... marital problems?" (Line 99) A <u>marital</u> problem refers to a problem between:
   - m) a brother and a sister
   - n) a boss and his or her employees
   - o) parents and their children
   - p) a husband and a wife

7) "'Tell them everything,' Roland urged her." (Line 101) To <u>urge</u> someone means to:
   - v) anger them
   - w) insist that they do something
   - x) change your relationship with them
   - y) tell them a secret

8) "In the end, I had to let him go." (Line 113) Which one of the following definitions for <u>let someone go</u> is correct in this sentence?
   - m) to stop holding someone
   - n) to forget about someone
   - o) to fire someone from a job
   - p) to give someone permission to go somewhere

9) "I just couldn't afford to keep him." (Line 114)

   If you can <u>afford</u> something, then you have

   enough M _o_ (_n_) _e_ _y_ for it.

10) "I thought he would be happy, but he was not. He complained all the time." (Line 122) Someone who <u>complains</u> focuses on the _____ parts of someone or something.
    - a) negative
    - b) surprising
    - c) interesting
    - d) detailed

11) "I think he was having an affair. I heard him talking on his cell phone many times outside the camera shop, when he was working." (Line 125) In this sentence, to <u>have an affair</u> means to:
   d) have a romantic relationship outside of your marriage
   e) have a business relationship outside of your job
   f) enjoy an activity that is not related to your work
   g) have an unhappy relationship with your friends

12) "He said, 'One of my bosses is going to give me a big Christmas bonus, and I mean a big one.'" (Line 144) In this sentence, <u>bonus</u> refers to:
   g) extra vacation time
   h) extra money
   i) extra job responsibilities
   j) extra work hours

B. Comprehension Questions

13) All of the following statements are true about Leo Mench's blackmail letter *except*:
   s) that the blackmailer wanted the money to be left in a garbage can
   t) that the letter included photos
   u) that the blackmailer wanted the money in a suitcase
   v) that the blackmailer wanted $50,000

14) Ellie feels like she failed to do her job in this chapter. What did she fail to do?
   s) She could not convince Roland Walker to talk about the blackmail letter.
   t) She was not the first person to tell Sara Sweet about the death of her husband.
   u) She did not ask Sara Sweet about her marital problems.
   v) She forgot to invite Officer Yokota to go to Sara Sweet's house.

15) Natalie Wells notices that Roland Walker isn't

   wearing a M a x r i g c

   R (i) t g .

16) Sara Sweet made all of these statements about her marriage *except*:
   p) "We never saw each other, and he was cold to me."
   q) "Things started to go bad when Terry lost his job."
   r) "He started to drink more and more. He yelled sometimes."
   s) "I wanted to have children, but Terry was never ready."

17) Which one of the following statements can we guess about Ellie?
   j) She thinks that driving is the worst part of being a police officer.
   k) She does not think that Roland Walker is good-looking.
   l) She wants to know Wells' opinions about the case.
   m) She suspects that Sara Sweet is guilty of the murder.

18) When did Leo Mench leave the purple suitcase in the garbage can?
   d) December 5th
   e) December 8th
   f) December 11th
   q) December 17th

19) Which piece of information from Sara Sweet surprised Roland Walker?
   c) that Terry might have been having an affair
   d) that Terry didn't know much about cameras even when he worked at Roland's camera shop
   e) that Terry was expecting a Christmas bonus
   f) that Terry used to be a police officer

20) Ellie noticed Roland Walker's

   ____ (__) ____ ____ ____ ____ ____ ____ near the stairs.

Now, go back to page 101 and fill in the puzzle answers to find out what the police officer said.

A. Police Briefing

Get into small groups and select a chief detective. The chief detective will lead group discussions, and make sure all members are participating.

1. Check your Chapter 2 puzzle answers with your group.

2. Discuss the evidence. Look back at the calendar on page 100. Does anything seem suspicious?

_____

_____

_____

B. Listen to the CD

TRACK 8

You will hear the call made by Billy Stemper to Sara Sweet, the wife of the victim. After you listen, answer the questions.

1. How did Billy know that Terry was the victim?

   _____

2. Billy seemed to realize that leaving this voice message was not a good idea. What two things did Billy say that show this?

   ☐ "He was killed some time last night inside the pawn shop."

   ☐ "I guess I'm talking too much. You must be in shock right now."

   ☐ "I'm sure she'll be coming to your house soon."

   ☐ "Then the detective came out to see me and she asked me all kinds of questions."

   ☐ "I should probably tell you face to face, but I guess it's too late for that now."

3. Did Billy do the right thing leaving this message on Sara's voicemail? Why or why not? Discuss.

C. Think Ahead

Think of three things that you would do next if you were Ellie.

1. ( ) _____ ☐

2. _____ ☐

3. _____ ☐

Now decide in what order she should do them. Write the order (1st, 2nd, 3rd) in the boxes on the right.

D. Quiz

Complete the quiz. You may use your Detective's Notebook, but close this book.

Chapter 3 : Pre-reading

Previously in *Whodunit... Blackmail*

The following panels show three important events from Chapter 2. Order and caption each panel.

Chapter 3 : The Videotape

In this chapter, Ellie discovers some important clues hidden in the Sweet home. She also interviews one more suspect, the beautiful and mysterious owner of the Cane Gallery.

• **Answer these pre-reading questions alone or with a partner. If you don't know the answer, guess.**

1. The police find a videotape in the Sweets' home. What do you think it might show?

    _____

    _____

2. Roland Walker helps Ellie in this chapter. How does Ellie seem to feel about Roland and his sister, Sara?

    _____

    _____

3. Ellie meets Ling Cane in this chapter. What do you already know about Ling?

    _____

    _____

Chapter 3

Crime Talk: alibi, blackmail, case, clue, murderer, suspicious

The Videotape

Ellie snuck outside the Sweet house when she had a free moment. It was 8:20 a.m., the perfect   1
time to call her daughter, Sofia.

"This is 9-1-1," Sofia answered. "What's your emergency?"

"I have a Code 7, a Code 7," Ellie countered, smiling. "I need back-up."

"There are no other cars in the area. I'm afraid that you're on your own." Sofia often pretended   5
to be a police officer. However, like most teenage girls, she was hoping to be a famous singer and
actress when she grew up.

"*Hola, mi amor,*" Ellie said, ending the game. "Did you get to school on time?"

"My first class starts in ten minutes. Are you on another hot case?"

Ellie liked to discuss her cases with Sofia, but not the murders. "Not really. Nothing too serious."   10

Sofia hesitated. "Well, be careful anyway."

Ellie's smile widened. Sofia was growing up so quickly. "Hey, who is the mother here? You or me?"

"I'm just saying," Sofia answered with a little embarrassment. "We're still going to Peru next
week, right?"

"We certainly are," Ellie answered. She needed a vacation badly. It was summer in Peru and she really wanted to visit her family for Christmas. And go to the beach.

Ellie saw Wells waving at her from inside the living room. "I'd better go. See you at home. *Un beso gigante.*"

Sofia made a kissing sound with her lips and hung up.

Inside the house, Sara was sitting on the sofa, talking on the phone. Roland was listening to his sister, but also looking at Ellie.

Wells pointed in the direction of the stairs. "They found something else," she whispered. "Up in the attic."

Moments later, Ellie and Wells were climbing a set of wooden stairs to the attic. The ceiling was low. Ellie had to duck under some wooden beams. She found an officer in the corner. "What did you find?" Ellie asked.

The officer stepped back so Ellie could see. "There was a hiding place under the floor board." There were two items—a videotape and a bundle of money.

"How much money?"

"Exactly one thousand dollars," the officer answered.

Natalie Wells spoke from behind. "That's odd. Why did he hide some money in the bedroom and more money up here?"

"Maybe this isn't his money," Ellie offered, thinking about Sara. "Let's watch the videotape."

There was an old VCR in the guest bedroom. Wells closed the door while Ellie turned on the TV.

After a few seconds, Wells exclaimed, "That's the vault in the pawn shop!" She was right. The videotape was from the security camera on the ceiling of the pawn shop. On the screen, Ellie could see Mench's back, the boxes of jewelry, and the file cabinets. The stack of paintings was there, with the Ross Curran on top. It looked much less beautiful on the black and white video. She could also see the lock outside the door.

"Wait a minute," Ellie mumbled. "Let's go back a little."

She pushed the rewind button. They watched Mench back out of the vault. The door closed behind him. His hand went up to the lock. "Here!" Ellie exclaimed, pressing play.

Just as she thought. The videotape clearly showed Mench entering the combination. 16-33-28.

"Well, I guess we know how Sweet got the combination to the vault," Wells said. "And look at the date."

In the corner of the screen was the date. "December 15th," Ellie muttered. "That was only two days ago. I thought the video camera was broken."

"I guess not," Wells said.

Ellie paused the VCR. "Remember that Sweet was in charge of the video camera." She scratched her head, thinking out loud. "So, Sweet lied to Mench. He told him that the camera was 50 broken. Then he secretly taped Mench entering the code." Ellie ejected the tape and gave it to Wells. "When you get back to the station, watch the rest. Maybe there will be another clue."

Back downstairs, Ellie asked Sara if she knew about the hiding place in the attic. She said that she did not. The officers were finished searching the house. It was time to go.

"Mrs. Sweet," Ellie said kindly, "I need to ask you to do something very difficult. We need for 55 you to identify your husband's body. Can you do that for us?"

Sara took a deep breath and nodded.

"Do you want me to come with you?" Roland asked.

"No, no," Sara said. "This is something I should do by myself."

"In that case," he said, turning to Ellie, "maybe I can help you. I have a security camera outside 60 my store. Maybe it will show something from last night."

He was right. Maybe his security camera showed Sweet walking down U Street. Maybe it showed Sweet's killer.

"Drop me off at the station with Mrs. Sweet," Wells offered. "I will make sure that she gets home afterwards." 65

Ellie looked at Sara Sweet. "Are you ready then?"

Soon they were in Ellie's car. Roland and Sara sat together in the back seat. It was a quiet ride back into Washington DC, giving Ellie a chance to think about the case. What did she know for sure? She knew that Sweet had a copy of the key to the pawn shop, probably Billy Stemper's. She knew how Sweet got the combination to the vault. She knew that Roland and Sara had reason to be angry with 70 Sweet. She knew that Sweet was blackmailing Leo Mench.

There was much more that she did not know. Did Sweet enter the pawn shop alone? Why did he open the vault? Was Mench lying about nothing being stolen from the vault? Did Mench know that Sweet was the blackmailer? Most importantly, why did someone kill Sweet?

When they arrived at the station, Ellie thanked Sara and let her out of the car. Roland also got 75 out of the car and gave his sister a long hug. They had a close relationship. Ellie had a thought: If one of them, Sara or Roland, killed Sweet, then the other one probably knew about it. Maybe they even did it together.

Ellie and Roland watched Sara and Wells disappear into the police station. Ellie looked up at the bright morning sky. The day was starting to heat up. 80

"Are you ready to go?" Ellie asked, already opening the back door.

Roland did not answer until Ellie looked at him. "Can I sit in the front?"

Ellie smiled, but just for a second. "That's against the rules. Sorry." Roland still did not move, so she added, "That's where we keep the big guns."

"Well, in that case…" Roland said, smiling. He eased into the backseat. Ellie started the car and pulled onto Wisconsin Avenue.

"It's difficult to talk through these things," Roland said. He meant the black, metal bars that separated the front seat and the back seat.

"You're right," she said, keeping her eyes on the road. "But they keep me safe."

"I'm not going to hurt you," he answered quickly. Was he flirting with her?

"Probably not," she said. "But just in case, I'm glad I have the bars." She wondered, *Am I flirting with him?*

The ride to U Street Camera was short, but full of conversation. Ellie learned that Roland was 39 years old, was divorced, and had a teenage daughter who lived with his ex-wife. He loved art, especially Ross Curran. He was saving money and hoping to buy a Ross Curran painting next year. He played soccer every Saturday and went to church every Sunday. Ellie did not talk about herself. It was important to stay professional with Mr. Roland Walker. He was part of a murder investigation.

U Street Camera Shop was nothing like Eagle Eye. The shelves and furniture looked modern. There were plenty of cameras and other items, but the store did not feel crowded. It felt a little like an art gallery.

Roland told Ellie that the security equipment was in a back room. Ellie entered but only saw a laptop computer. "No TV?" she asked.

Roland gave her a big smile. "My security camera is more modern than Leo's. The camera records onto a disc, not a tape." He inserted a mini CD into the computer and they waited for an image to appear. When it did, Ellie saw the front door of the camera shop, the front windows, and part of the sidewalk.

"The camera turns on at 9:00 at night and runs until 5:00 in the morning," Roland told her.

"What time did Terry start working?"

"Ten o'clock."

"Well, let's start there."

They first saw Terry walking outside the store at 10:08 p.m.. They fast-forwarded and saw him walking again at 10:44.

"Where did he sit when we wasn't walking around?" Ellie asked, notebook in hand.

"The art gallery has a small lobby. Terry could not enter the gallery, but he had a key for the lobby. He had a chair and a small desk there."

On the screen, pedestrians walked by the windows, but no one looked suspicious. Roland continued to fast-forward. Terry walked by every 30 or 40 minutes, always in the direction of the pawn shop. At 11:52 he had his cell phone in his hand. Ellie asked Roland to pause the recording. Then she slipped out and made a quick phone call.

"Kaz, do you have Sweet's phone records yet?"

"Not yet. Soon."

"Call me when you do."

Back on the screen, Sweet walked by the camera shop at 12:23 a.m. He passed again at 12:55, 1:21, and 1:58. That was the last time they saw him. Pedestrians continued to walk by until 2:34. Then they saw no one until 3:33. Ellie guessed that the murder happened in that hour. At 4:48 they pressed play because a woman ran by screaming. This was certainly the woman who saw the body. At 5:00 a.m., the recording ended.

Security camera timeline: Use this timeline to organize the evidence from Roland's security camera. What happened at each of the times shown below? Write in the details.

Time	Details
10:08 p.m.	Terry walks by shop.
10:44	
11:52	
12:23, 12:55, 1:21, and 1:58 a.m.	
1:58 - 2:34	
2:34 - 3:33	
4:48	
5:00	

"My security camera wasn't very helpful," Roland said. He ejected the CD and handed it to Ellie. "Sorry."

"Don't be sorry. We didn't see Terry's murderer, but we know more about when the crime happened. At the station we'll watch the CD more carefully."

There was a silence. Ellie was not sure what else to say. From outside the door, a woman's shouting broke the silence.

"Roland, are you in there? Roland!"

Ellie and Roland left the back room. A woman was just inside the store. She had long black 135

hair, all the way down her back. She was pretty, shorter than Ellie, and dressed in red from neck to toe.

"I'm here, Ling," Roland said. "This is Detective Koo."

"I just heard what happened," Ling said. "I came in to open the gallery and saw all of the

police cars. Is it true about Terry?"

When Roland did not answer, the owner of the Cane Gallery looked to Ellie. Ellie introduced 140

herself and gave Ling Cane the basic facts of the crime. Ling wiped her tears with the corner of her red

scarf.

"I'm going to need to ask you a few questions," Ellie told her.

"Of course," Ling answered quickly. "Go on."

Ellie looked at Roland. He understood. "I should go," he said. "I need some clothes if I'm 145

going to stay with my sister. I'll be in touch." He was quiet for a moment, then added: "If I think of

anything else."

Ling Cane led Ellie to the Cane Gallery. She used a key to open the front door. In the corner

of the lobby were Sweet's desk and chair. Both women took a long look. The lamp was turned off. A

sports magazine was opened to a story about college football. 150

"Poor Terry," Ling said. She was entering a code on a security panel. There was a loud beep.

Then she opened the door to the gallery. There were no security cameras.

"Did Terry know the security code?" Ellie asked, following Ling inside.

"No, I use a private security company. If the alarm goes off, they call the police. Terry only had

a key to the lobby." 155

Ellie looked around the gallery. One wall had about ten Ross Curran paintings on it. The other

walls displayed different artists.

"I love Curran's work," Ellie said, studying a huge green and brown painting. "So colorful. This

one looks like a forest."

"Actually, that one is called The Dinner Party." 160

Ellie stepped back and looked again. She did not see a dinner party anywhere in the painting.

Well, it was still beautiful.

"Curran sells all of his art here?" Ellie asked.

"That's right," Ling said. She offered Ellie a chair and they both sat down at a counter. "I have

more than thirty of Ross' paintings here." 165

Ellie was confused. "Where are the rest?"

"Back in the vault." Ling nodded to the back of the store. "Would you like some coffee?"

"No, no thanks," Ellie said. Too much coffee already. "And how many Currans do you have at your gallery in Singapore?"

"I would have to ask my brother. Maybe ten." 170

Ellie and Ling talked for about ten minutes. Ling's husband, Carson, was a computer salesman. He was out of town, in Philadelphia. They lived in a condo in Bethesda, Maryland, about thirty minutes away. They had no children. Like all of the others, Ling had no alibi and did not own a gun.

Ellie's phone rang. It was Yokota. Ellie stayed in her chair and answered.

"I checked Terry Sweet's phone records," Yokota said. "I found something very interesting…" 175

"___ ___ ___ ___ ___   ___ ___ ___   ___ ___ ___ ___   ___ ___ ___ ___
16 19 10 3   5   12 18 8   6   18 4   17   2   9   20 15

___ ___ ___ ___ ___   ___ ___ ___ ___ ___ ___ ___ ___ ___ ___ ___ ___ ___
1   12 9   20 10   14 9   20 11 3   13 16 18 5   7   9   4   16

___ ___ ___ ___   ___ ___ ___ ___   ___ ___ ___ ___."
19 7   5   12   2   7   20 15   14 18 4   10

"Continue," Ellie said casually, not looking at Ling.

Yokota went on. "Their phone records go back about three weeks. They talked almost every day. They last spoke at about midnight last night."

"Thank you, Officer," Ellie said. "I'm with someone. I'll call you back in a few minutes."

Ellie hung up but did not say a word to Ling. Ling wiggled uncomfortably in her chair, but 180 also stayed quiet. Finally Ellie said softly, "So, how well did you know Terry Sweet?"

"Well, he was a nice man. He…" Ling stopped talking. Ellie was staring at her, not even blinking. Ling wiped her forehead. Then she put her hands flat on the counter. Finally she whispered, "What do you want to ask me, Detective Koo?"

Ellie stood up very straight. "What do you want to tell me, Mrs. Cane?" 185

CHAPTER 3: PUZZLE

Instructions:

To discover what Yokota said, answer the following vocabulary and comprehension questions. After you have answered all of the questions, use the letters of the correct responses and the circled letters to solve the puzzle on page 113.

A. Vocabulary Questions

1) "There are no other cars in the area. I'm afraid that you're on your own." (Line 5)

   If you do something <u>on your own</u>, then you will

   not get any: H _e_ _l_ (_p_) .

2) "Moments later, Ellie and Wells were climbing a set of wooden stairs to the attic." (Line 24) The <u>attic</u> is usually the:
   j) space where cars are parked
   k) space inside the walls of a house
   l) space between the roof and the top floor
   m) space under the first floor

3) "The videotape was from the security camera on the ceiling of the pawn shop." (Line 36) You might find all of these on a <u>ceiling</u> except:
   d) a fan
   e) a carpet
   f) a vent
   g) a smoke alarm

4) "She pushed the 'rewind' button. They watched Mench back out of the vault." (Line 41) Which group of words is associated with the word <u>rewind</u>?
   n) play, stop, pause
   o) jump, fall, hop
   p) drive, brake, shift
   q) open, close, emergency

   How are rewind and the other three words related?

   _____

5) "It was a quiet ride back into Washington DC, giving Ellie a chance to think about the case. What did she know for sure?" (Line 68)

   If you <u>know something for sure</u>, then you know

   that it is (_t_) _r_ _u_ _e_ .

6) "He meant the black, metal bars that separated the front seat and the back seat" (Line 87) Which definition of <u>bar</u> matches the meaning in the sentence?
   k) a place that serves alcohol
   l) a block; a thick piece of something
   m) a stick; a pole; a rod
   n) a long piece of candy, especially chocolate

7) "Was he flirting with her?" (Line 90) <u>Flirting</u> with someone is a(n) ___way to show that you ___ him or her romantically.
   g) direct; like
   h) direct; dislike
   i) indirect; like
   j) indirect; dislike

8) "They fast-forwarded and saw him walking again at 10:44." (Line 111)

   Which vocabulary word from this chapter is the *opposite* of <u>fast-forward</u>?

   _r_ _e_ _w_ _i_ _n_ (_d_)

9) "The art gallery has a small lobby. Terry could not enter the gallery, but he had a key for the lobby." (Line 114) A <u>lobby</u> is a room:
   l) where extra items are stored
   m) with no windows or doors
   n) underneath the floor
   o) near the entrance of a building

10) "He ejected the tape and handed it to Ellie." (Line 128) All of the following can be <u>ejected</u> *except*:
    e) a remote control from a TV
    f) a drink from a vending machine
    g) a DVD from a DVD player
    h) a memory card from a digital camera

    What does it mean to eject something?

    _____

11) "She was entering a code on a security panel." (Line 151) A security panel will probably have all of the following except:
    u) lights
    v) cameras
    w) buttons
    x) numbers

12) "One wall had about ten Ross Curran paintings on it. The other walls displayed different artists." (Line 156)

    A word with the same meaning as display is:

    S (h) o w .

B. Comprehension Questions

13) What does Terry Sweet's videotape explain?
    r) how Terry knew the combination to the vault
    s) what Terry wanted to steal from the vault
    t) how Terry got a copy of the key to the pawn shop
    u) what time Terry broke into the pawn shop

14) Ellie believes that Terry Sweet was killed _____.
    b) before 2:34 a.m.
    c) between 2:34 a.m. and 3:33 a.m.
    d) between 3:33 a.m. and 4:48 a.m.
    e) after 4:48 a.m.

15) Which one of the following statements can we guess about Sofia?
    g) She worries about her mother when Ellie is at work.
    h) She is going to miss her boyfriend when she is on vacation in Peru.
    i) She never answers her cellular phone when she is at school.
    j) She will be a police officer when she grows up.

16) All of the following are true about the Cane Gallery except:
    q) that it has many Ross Curran paintings
    r) that it is protected by a private security company
    s) that it has a small lobby near the back door
    t) that it contains a vault

17) Terry Sweet only had a key to the Cane Gallery's

    s t o r (g).

18) What happened on December 15th?
    a) Terry videotaped Mench opening the vault.
    b) Mench paid the blackmailer by putting the money in the purple suitcase.
    c) Terry received his Christmas bonus.
    d) Terry was killed inside the pawn shop.

19) Why does Sara Sweet have to go to the police station?
    t) She must give an official statement about the crime.
    u) She must show a videotape to the police.
    v) She is under arrest for the crime.
    w) She must identify her husband's body.

20) Ellie has discovered all of the following things about Ling Cane except:
    l) that she lives in Bethesda, Maryland
    m) that her husband Carson is a computer salesman
    n) that she goes to church every Sunday
    o) that she does not own a gun

Now, go back to page 113 and fill in the puzzle answers to find out what Yokota said.

A. Police Briefing

Get into small groups and select a chief detective. The chief detective will lead group discussions, and make sure all members are participating.

1. Check your Chapter 3 puzzle answers with your group.

2. Discuss the evidence and complete the box below.

What new facts did Ellie discover in this chapter? Are there any new suspects? Any new clues? What do you think about them?

New evidence/suspects/information	What do you think?

B. **TRACK + 9**   **Listen to the CD**

You will hear the coroner's autopsy examination. After you listen, answer the questions.

1. What probably caused the wound on Terry's head?

   _____

2. How did Dr. Martinez estimate the time of death?

   _____

3. What questions do you still have about how Terry Sweet was killed? Discuss.

C. Think Ahead

Think of different questions that Ellie should ask each of these possible suspects.

Leo Mench _____

Billy Stemper _____

Roland Walker _____

Sara Sweet _____

Ling Cane _____

D. Quiz

Complete the quiz. You may use your Detective's Notebook, but close this book.

Pre-reading

Previously in *Whodunit... The Videotape*

The following panels show three important events from Chapter 3. Order and caption each panel.

The Letter

In this chapter, Ellie discovers more secrets that tie all of the suspects to the not-so-innocent victim. It seems that everyone had a motive for killing bad boy Terry Sweet.

• **Answer these pre-reading questions alone or with a partner. If you don't know the answer, guess.**

1. How do you think Ling Cane explains her connection to Terry Sweet?

_____

_____

2. The police find a love letter in this chapter. The letter connects two of the suspects. Who do you think sent the letter? Who received it?

_____

_____

3. You have now read half of *Death on U Street*. Can you guess who killed Terry Sweet and why?

_____

_____

_____

Chapter 4

The Letter

Ling stood up and walked to the front door of the gallery. Ellie did not move.

"I do not want to answer any more questions," Ling said boldly.

"I see," said Ellie, crossing her legs. "The problem is that you must answer my questions. You can answer them right here, right now, or we can do this later at the station. It's your choice."

Ling had her hand on the door handle. She could not see that Ellie's fingers were brushing the handle of her gun. Just in case. Finally Ling said, "Fine, I admit it. I was having an affair with Terry. Is that what you want to hear?"

"I want to hear the truth," Ellie said, relaxing her hand.

Ling lowered her voice and returned to the counter. "My husband doesn't know. Sara Sweet doesn't know. Please don't tell them."

Ellie stood up and put her hands on her hips. She was not usually taller than the suspects. "If I were you, I wouldn't worry about what your husband and Sara know. Terry is dead. You had a relationship with him. That is a much bigger problem."

Ling looked at Ellie with a shocked expression. "But I didn't kill him! Why would I kill Terry?"

Ellie did not answer, but she could think of many reasons. Maybe Terry wanted to end the relationship, or tell Ling's husband. Maybe Ling wanted to end it, but Terry did not. She was sure that Ling had more secrets.

"Tell me everything," Ellie finally said, taking out her notebook. "Every detail."

According to Ling, she and Terry started the affair about three weeks earlier. They met several mornings at Terry's house, when Sara was working. Ling and Terry were happy together, but did not want to break up with their spouses.

"It wasn't serious," Ling explained. "I love my husband and don't want to leave him."

"Love? That is how you show your love?" Ellie asked quietly, trying to upset Ling a little, hoping she would say more.

"I'm not proud of myself," Ling whispered. "You have to understand that my husband Carson works all the time. He is always out of town on business. He is out of town now. I get lonely."

"When was the last time you were with Terry?"

Ling buried her head in her hands, and then pulled back her long hair. "Let's see. Today is Wednesday. Monday morning, I guess. Yes, Monday."

"Did you tell anyone else about your relationship?"

"Absolutely not. Nobody knows."

Ellie walked around for a few moments, studying the art. She still could not see any dinner party in the painting. "Mrs. Cane, do you have any proof of your relationship with Terry?"

"No," Ling answered after a long pause. "Well, you could check my phone records. We talked often. And I can tell you what his house looks like."

Ling described the house perfectly. Ellie was not sure what to think, but had no more questions.

"Don't leave town," Ellie said, walking to the door. "We're not done."

Ling again begged Ellie not to tell her husband about the affair. Ellie walked outside without a word.

Ellie walked past U Street Camera. It was empty, no sign of Roland. A curious crowd waited outside Eagle Eye Pawn Shop. Ellie slipped through them and showed her ID to an officer. Then she was back in Leo Mench's colorful, crowded store. Officers were still examining the scene.

Ellie stopped in front of the vault. The chalk outline of Sweet's body blocked the entrance. "What were you doing here?" she whispered to the outline. "What did you want from this vault?"

Ellie felt certain that she was missing something. There must be a clue somewhere. She examined the video camera. It was pointing straight down. Certainly Sweet moved it after taping Mench opening the vault. She checked the cash register and the floor underneath. She went back to

15

20

25

30

35

40

45

look at the door and the window. She used her flashlight to look inside all of the vents. She put her hands on her hips and looked in every direction. Nothing seemed broken or out of place. She was missing something. 50

In the vault, she looked over everything once more. She moved boxes of jewelry and thumbed through the paintings. She checked the walls for hidden panels. Nothing.

Then she heard a strange noise. It was her stomach rumbling.

"I'm going back to the station," she said to no one. "Time for lunch." 55

A turkey sandwich was waiting for Ellie on her desk, which she ate with her coat on. There was also a report about the fragments of wood that she found on and near Sweet's body. She checked her email and found an audio attachment explaining the findings, which she listened to while she popped grapes in her mouth. The wood was pine with a dark brown finish on it. It was probably from a piece of furniture. Ellie thought back to Eagle Eye Pawn Shop. There was furniture everywhere, but she 60 did not remember any of it being broken. On her desk was also a copy of Leo Mench's bank records. Indeed, he withdrew $10,000 from his savings account on Saturday, December 6th. Ellie finished her lunch and the reports, and then found Natalie Wells at the vending machine.

"Yokota said that all of the neighbors were interviewed," Wells said, pulling a bag of pretzels out of the machine. "No one saw anything unusual, and no one heard a gunshot." 65

Ellie nodded. "Did Sara Sweet identify her husband's body?"

It was Wells' turn to nod. "She did."

"And is Roland Walker here?"

Wells gave her a long look, and then answered, "He got here about ten minutes ago. He and Sara are giving written statements." 70

Ellie told Wells all about Ling Cane. Wells asked what their next move should be.

"I need you to check on a few things for me," Ellie said. After giving Wells the details, she added: "I am going to pay a visit to Mr. Mench."

Ellie found Leo Mench in a holding cell in the basement. A guard opened the door for her and she slipped inside. The cell was warm, but Ellie kept her long black coat on. She buried her hands in 75 the pockets, waiting for Mench to speak.

"Well?" he finally asked. He was sitting on the cell's small bed, looking annoyed.

"You still don't want to tell me?" she asked.

"I don't want to tell you anything," he snapped.

"So you enjoy being behind bars? 80

Nothing.

"You don't want to tell me why Terry Sweet was blackmailing you?"

"No, I don't want to…" Then he stopped, realizing what Ellie had said. "What do you mean? It was Terry blackmailing me?"

Ellie was not sure if Mench was truly surprised. She told him about the purple suitcase and the $500. 85

"Five hundred?" he repeated. "Where was the rest of it? I gave him ten thousand dollars!"

She ignored his question. "I think you knew that Terry was blackmailing you."

"I swear that I didn't know," he insisted. "Can I please get out of here?"

"You took evidence from a crime scene," Ellie said flatly, waving to the guard. "You're not going anywhere." 90

"Wait!" Mench cried out. Ellie waited, but he said nothing else.

"What?"

"My son. Can I call my son, Noah?"

Ellie looked at the guard. "He already used his one phone call," the guard explained. 95

"I'm sorry," Ellie said. "You know that suspects only get to make one phone call. If you decide that you want to cooperate, then I can probably get you another phone call."

When Mench turned away, Ellie left the cell. She lifted her hand to call the elevator, but it opened in front of her. A hurried Yokota stepped out.

"I was looking for you," he said. 100

"You found me," she replied quickly.

He handed her a plastic evidence bag. "They found this in Terry Sweet's car."

Inside the bag was a crumpled piece of paper. Ellie borrowed a pair of gloves from Yokota and opened the bag. She read the paper twice, and then looked at Yokota.

"He's here now," Yokota said. "That's why I ran to find you. I put him in Interview Room 2." 105

The elevator was already gone. She patted Yokota on the back and opened the door to the stairs. She did not stop to catch her breath until she was outside the interview room.

"What's going on?" Billy Stemper asked when Ellie opened the door. "Why did they put me in this room?"

"You were already in the station?" Ellie asked, ignoring his question. 110

"Giving a written statement," Billy answered. "Then they told me to wait in here."

Billy had changed out of his pajamas. He was now wearing a Washington Redskins sweatshirt and a pair of green sweatpants. His hair looked like a bird's nest.

"Can I give you some advice?" Ellie asked, slipping the paper out of the plastic bag. She did not wait for him to answer. "The next time you write a love letter to a married woman, don't put your name on it." 115

The color left Billy's face. Ellie smoothed the paper out and put it on the table in front of Billy. Over his shoulder, she read it again:

> Sara, I am too afraid to tell you this face to face. There is something you must know. I love you. I have loved you since I met you. Terry does not treat you well. He does not deserve you. I want to be with you, Sara. Please think about it. I await your answer. Love, Billy

Billy was silent, eyes closed. Ellie took a seat in front of him. "Do you want to know where we found your love letter?" 120

Billy kept his eyes closed. "I doubt it," he muttered.

"In Terry's car, Billy. It was in his car."

Billy's eyes were open now. "No, no, no. How did he get it? Oh, no. Terry knew? He knew?"

Billy looked surprised and sounded scared, but Ellie could not be sure. "He didn't say anything to you about it?" 125

"No, no," Billy repeated. "Are you sure that it was in his car?"

"When did you give this letter to Sara?"

"Not long ago. About three weeks." Billy put his trembling hands in his lap.

"You gave it to her in person?" Ellie asked, waiting for Billy to nod. "What did she say?"

"I left before she read it. I was too embarrassed. She called me the next day. She wasn't interested. She just wanted to be friends. That was the end of it." 130

Ellie put the letter back into the bag, taking her time. Finally she asked, "How did that make you feel, Billy?"

"Terrible," he quickly answered. "It felt terrible."

"It made you angry," she said, nodding. 135

"Yes. I mean no. I wasn't angry. I was just disappointed."

"You wrote that Terry treated Sara badly. What did you mean?"

Billy leaned back in the chair and looked to the ceiling. "I can't believe this is happening," he said. He sat up straight. "I just meant that he wasn't nice to her. He was always telling me about how they would fight. He called her bad names and made jokes about her. He said that she was getting old, 140

Chapter 4: The Letter |123

that she wasn't as pretty as she used to be. He was mean. He didn't respect her."

Ellie just sat and nodded. Finally she said, "This doesn't look good, Billy."

"What do you mean? Do you think I killed him?"

Ellie was not sure what to think. Billy said that he gave Sara the letter about three weeks ago. Ling claimed that she and Sweet started their affair three weeks ago. Could the two be related? From what people said, Sweet was a violent man. If he found this letter, wouldn't he confront Billy Stemper? 145

Ellie flipped open her phone and called the front desk. The officer told her that Sara and Roland were ready to leave.

"Don't let them leave," she said. "I need to talk to Mrs. Sweet."

Billy closed his eyes again. He whispered, "No, no, no." 150

They put Sara in Interview Room 3. Ellie sat down across from her and showed her the letter.

"You went to my office?" Sara asked angrily.

"Your office?"

"My office. The letter was at the bottom of my desk drawer."

Ellie felt sorry for Sara. She felt even worse when she told Sara where the letter was found. 155

"His car! His car?" Sara was shaking.

"Billy said that he gave you the letter about three weeks ago."

"Yeah, he came to my office to give it to me. I remember that it was the day after Thanksgiving, so I guess it was November 29th. I had to work. It was sweet, but I told him no. I don't think of Billy that way." She took a deep breath. "Terry had the letter?" she asked again. 160

Ellie grasped Sara's hand to keep it from shaking. "Did Terry go to your office after Billy gave you the letter?"

Sara nodded. "There was one time, about a week ago. I was in a meeting when he got there. He waited at my desk." Sara's eyes filled with tears. "I can't believe he went through my desk. I can't believe he knew about Billy's letter." 165

"Why did you keep the letter?" Ellie asked gently.

Sara shook her head. "I don't know. I just did. I never thought Terry would see it."

"Hold on a minute," Ellie muttered, taking her notebook out of her coat pocket. She flipped through the pages, and then said, "You told me that Terry said something strange to you about a week ago. The Thursday before last Thursday, so December 4th. He said that the 'three of you' would have a long talk and he seemed angry." Ellie paused and then looked at Sara. "Think carefully. Was this the same day he went to your office to see you?" 170

Sara thought for a moment. Then she exclaimed, "It was! He was talking about Billy, wasn't he? He found Billy's letter and maybe thought that I was seeing Billy."

"I think so," Ellie agreed.

"Then why didn't he say anything to me or Billy?" she asked, starting to cry again.

"I don't know," Ellie lied. In truth, Ellie thought that she did know. Terry told his wife about a Christmas bonus that he was going to receive. This was certainly the blackmail money from Leo Mench. Terry probably did not want to say anything to his wife or Billy until after he got the money. But then Ellie frowned. Leo dropped off his purple suitcase on December 11th, six days ago. Terry had Leo's money. So why didn't he confront Sara and Billy about the letter?

The love letter: How did Billy's letter get into Ellie's hand? Show the history of Billy's letter. Describe what happened on each of the days below.

Sara, I am too afraid to . . .

November 29th	December 4th	December 17th

Ellie gave Sara a tissue and told her that she could go. When they stepped outside, an officer pulled Ellie aside. "Billy Stemper wants to see you. He says it's important."

Ellie entered Interview Room 2 again. Billy was still seated at the table. He looked exhausted.

"I have something else to tell you," he began. "I should have told you this morning."

Ellie waited, giving Billy time to speak his mind.

"Do you know about the robbery that happened about six months ago?" he asked.

"Mench told me," Ellie said. "He said that someone broke the windows of the Cane Gallery. Then someone broke into the camera shop."

Billy rubbed his eyes. Then he blinked and said...

175

180

185

190

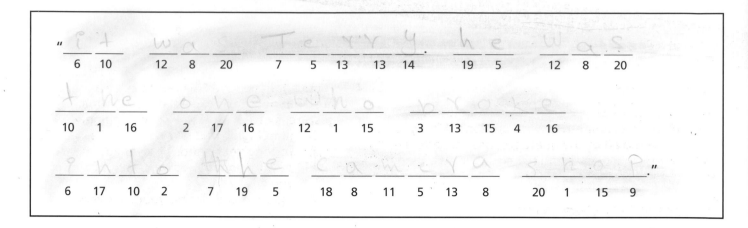

"<u>i</u> <u>t</u> <u>w</u> <u>a</u> <u>s</u> <u>T</u> <u>e</u> <u>r</u> <u>r</u> <u>y</u>. <u>h</u> <u>e</u> <u>w</u> <u>a</u> <u>s</u>
  6 10   12 8 20   7 5 13 13 14   19 5   12 8 20

<u>t</u> <u>h</u> <u>e</u> <u>o</u> <u>n</u> <u>e</u> <u>w</u> <u>h</u> <u>o</u> <u>b</u> <u>r</u> <u>o</u> <u>k</u> <u>e</u>
 10 1 16   2 17 16   12 1 15   3 13 15 4 16

<u>i</u> <u>n</u> <u>t</u> <u>o</u> <u>t</u> <u>h</u> <u>e</u> <u>c</u> <u>a</u> <u>m</u> <u>e</u> <u>r</u> <u>a</u> <u>s</u> <u>h</u> <u>o</u> <u>p</u>."
 6 17 10 2   7 19 5   18 8 11 5 13 8   20 1 15 9

Ellie, who was standing by the door, finally sat down. "And how do you know this?"

Billy settled back in his chair. "I have a friend who works at a pawn shop in Silver Spring. He came by Eagle Eye about a month ago. Terry was there, and my friend recognized him. He said, 'That guy came by my shop a few weeks ago. He tried to sell me a bunch of cameras.' I asked him more about the cameras. They were the same cameras that were stolen from U Street."

"Are you sure?"

"The thief stole six cameras. My friend described them all."

END OF CHAPTER 4 END OF CHAPTER 4 END OF CHAPTER 4

Instructions:

To discover what Billy said, answer the following vocabulary and comprehension questions. After you have answered all of the questions, use the letters of the correct responses and the circled letters to solve the puzzle on page 126.

A. Vocabulary Questions

1) "Ellie stood up and put her hands on her hips." (Line 11) Which picture shows someone with their <u>hands on their hips</u>?

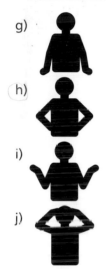

g)

h)

i)

j)

2) "According to Ling, she and Terry started the affair about three weeks earlier." (Line 19) The phrase <u>according to Ling</u> as used here means:
    l) Ling apologized because...
    m) Ling was the reason that...
    n) Ling didn't want to but...
    o) Ling said that...

3) "Ling and Terry were happy together, but did not want to break up with their <u>spouses</u>." (Line 21)

Spouse is another word for

H _u_ _s_ (_b_) _a_ _h_ _d_ or

_w_ _i_ _f_ _e_ .

4) "Ling again begged Ellie not to tell her husband about the affair." (Line 39) Which gesture is often associated with <u>begging</u>?
    i) jumping up and down
    j) putting your hands up over your head
    k) putting your hands together in front of you
    l) opening and closing your eyes very quickly

What does it mean to beg for something?

_____

5) "The wood was pine with a dark brown finish on it." (Line 59) Which one of the following wood products would *not* usually have a <u>finish</u> on it?
    d) a wooden table
    e) a piece of firewood
    f) a baseball bat
    g) a wooden cane

6) "There was furniture everywhere, but she did not remember any of it being broken." (Line 60) All of the following are examples of <u>furniture</u> *except*:
    i) a ceiling fan
    j) a bed
    k) a dining room table
    l) a sofa

7) "He [Roland] got here about ten minutes ago. He and Sara are giving written statements." (Line 70)

The police might ask for a <u>statement</u> if you have

I N ___ ___ ___ ___ ___ (___) ___ ___ ___

about a case.

8) "If you decide that you want to cooperate, then I can probably get you another phone call." (Line 97) To <u>cooperate</u> means to:
    z) try to win
    a) work together
    b) have good luck
    c) try something new

9) "Inside the bag was a crumpled piece of paper."
(Line 103) Where would you usually expect to
find a crumpled piece of paper?
   m) inside a newspaper
   n) in a file cabinet
   o) on a teacher's desk
   p) in a garbage can

Why would you crumple up a piece of paper?

_____

10) "Billy put his trembling hands in his lap."
(Line 128) You only have a lap when you:
   t) sit down
   u) jump into the air
   v) lie down
   w) run

Why is a laptop computer called a laptop?

_____

11) "Ling claimed that she and Sweet started their
affair three weeks ago." (Line 145) If you claim
something, then you state that it is:
   l) untrue
   m) true
   n) impossible
   o) sad

12) "'Hold on a minute,' Ellie muttered, taking
her notebook out of her coat pocket."
(Line 168)

Another word for hold on is:

(S) T O P .

B. Comprehension Questions

13) Ling admits that she was having a(n)

A _ _ _ a _ _ (V) with Terry.

14) Ling tells Ellie all of the following except:
   w) that she was lonely because her husband
      was always out of town
   x) that she told no one about the affair
   y) that she last saw Terry on Tuesday morning.
   z) that she and Terry started the affair about
      three weeks earlier

15) Ellie finds all of the following on her desk
except:
   l) her lunch
   m) Leo Mench's bank records
   n) a report about the fragments of wood
   o) a love letter from Billy to Sara

16) Why does Ellie return to Eagle Eye Pawn Shop
in this chapter?
   c) to look for broken pieces of furniture
   d) to try to open the vault with the
      combination from the videotape
   e) to look for more clues
   f) to examine the pawn shop's videotapes

17) Mench asks Ellie if he can speak with his

_ _ _ (L) , but Ellie says no.

18) What did Sara do after she received Billy's
letter?
   b) She started an affair with Billy.
   c) She told Billy that she liked him, but not
      romantically.
   d) She told Terry about the letter.
   e) She crumpled up the letter and put it in
      her car.

19) Terry told Sara about his Christmas bonus on
the same day that he:
   h) found Billy's letter
   i) started an affair with Ling
   j) got the purple suitcase
   k) discovered the code for Mench's vault

20) Ellie thinks that she knows the answers to all of
these questions, except one. Which question
can she not answer?
   q) Why did Ling and Terry talk on the
      phone so often?
   r) Who was blackmailing Leo Mench?
   s) Why didn't Terry confront his wife and
      Billy?
   t) How did Terry get Billy's letter?

**Now, go back to page 126 and fill in the puzzle
answers to find out what Billy said.**

A. Police Briefing

Get into small groups and select a chief detective. The chief detective will lead group discussions, and make sure all members are participating.

1. Check your Chapter 4 puzzle answers with your group.

2. Discuss the evidence and complete the box below.

> List the possible motives that each suspect had. If you have another suspect in mind, discuss him or her on the final line. Who does your group think is most likely to be the killer?

Billy Stemper _____

Leo Mench _____

Roland Walker _____

Sara Sweet _____

Ling Cane _____

Someone else? _____

B. **Listen to the CD**

You will hear a report from the doctor at the crime lab about the wood fragments found on and around Terry Sweet's body. After you listen, answer the questions.

1. Why did Dr. Henry mistakenly think that the wood was oak?

   _____

2. What does Dr. Henry think is the source of the wood fragments? He gives <u>two</u> possibilities.

   _____

3. Based on Dr. Henry's report, where do you think the wood might have come from? Discuss.

C. Think Ahead

Which of these do you think is most likely? Number them from 1 to 5, with 1 being most likely and 5 being lest likely.

☐ Terry was killed because of a romantic relationship.

☐ Terry was killed for revenge.

☐ Terry was killed because he was trying to steal something.

☐ Terry was killed by accident.

☐ Other: _____

D. Quiz

Complete the quiz. You may use your Detective's Notebook, but close this book.

Chapter 5 : Pre-reading

Previously in *Whodunit... The Letter*

The following panels show three important events from Chapter 4. Order and caption each panel.

....

Chapter 5 : The Meeting

In this chapter, Ellie meets with another very mysterious character and learns some surprising facts about the owner of the Cane Gallery and her husband. Meanwhile, the charming Roland Walker reveals that he also knew more than he admitted.

• **Answer these pre-reading questions alone or with a partner. If you don't know the answer, guess.**

1. The police make a suspicious discovery about Carson Cane in this chapter. What do you think it could be?

   _____

2. Ellie and Roland Walker have an argument in this chapter. What do you think they argue about?

   _____

3. In the group discussion at the end of chapter 4, your group thought about the most likely suspect. What do you think about this choice? Do you have a different opinion?

   _____

   _____

The Meeting

Ellie stared at Billy Stemper. The Eagle Eye Pawn Shop employee seemed very sure. He believed that Terry Sweet was guilty of stealing cameras from U Street Camera Shop. That would mean that Terry stole from Roland, his brother-in-law. 1

Ellie started thinking out loud. "Your friend came into your shop a month ago. He said that Terry came to see him a few weeks before that. But the cameras were stolen six months ago." 5

Billy leaned in. "I have a theory about that. I think that Terry hid the cameras for a few months, hoping that people would forget about the robbery. Then he tried to sell them."

"Did your friend buy the cameras?"

"No. He made Terry an offer, but Terry wanted more money."

"Maybe your friend was mistaken. Maybe it just looked like Terry, or maybe they were different cameras?" 10

Billy shrugged his shoulders and yawned. He seemed comfortable for the first time. Ellie didn't like that. "And you decided not to tell the police?"

Billy looked away. "I wanted to, but he told me not to."

"He?" Ellie asked. 15

"Roland," Billy said quietly. "I told Roland about it, and he told me not to tell anyone else."

Now it was Ellie's turn to close her eyes. "When did you tell Mr. Walker about your suspicion?"

"I told him when I found out, a month ago."

"Did he believe you?"

"I don't know. I think so. He told me not to worry about it. He said that he would handle it." 20

Ellie was finished with Billy. She told Yokota that she needed to see Roland Walker. Then she sat in the quiet interview room and thought about the case. In her notebook, she drew a long rectangle in the middle of the next page and wrote 'Roland Walker' inside. Then she drew circles and connected them to the Roland rectangle with arrows. In the circles she wrote: 'suspected that T.S. robbed his store'; 'suspected that T.S. was having affair'; 'would do anything to protect sister'. 25

Ellie then added one page for each suspect in the case.

'Sara Sweet: suspected T.S. having an affair'; 'unhappy marriage'; 'kept love note from B.S.'

'Billy Stemper: in love with S.S.'; 'told R.W. about the camera robbery'; 'lives close to the shop'; 'missing key'.

'Leo Mench: blackmailed by T.S.'; 'stole letter from vault'; 'won't tell the truth about blackmail'. 30

'Ling Cane: having affair with T.S.'; 'phone records'.

Then Ellie added two circles to each page: 'no alibi'; 'doesn't own a gun'.

A knock on the door brought Ellie back to the real world. She sat up straight, ready to confront Roland Walker. She was surprised when Natalie Wells entered instead. 35

"I have news," she said, closing the door behind her. "I just got a call from Carson Cane's hotel in Philadelphia. He isn't there. He was never there."

Ellie turned back a few pages in her notebook. "Are you sure?"

"A hotel employee just left a message on my cell phone. Cane's company paid for his room, but he never checked in. I called his company, but no one answered. I left a message for them to call me 40 back." Wells scratched her head. "What do you think this means?"

"I'm not sure," Ellie said. "Ling Cane says that her husband has been out of town for three days. She also says that she went to Terry Sweet's house on Monday." Ellie looked up at Wells. "Maybe Carson Cane suspected that his wife was having an affair. Maybe he followed her on Monday when she went to Terry's house." 45

"I think I need to find Carson Cane," Wells said plainly.

"I think you're right," Ellie agreed. "Let me know what you find out."

Ellie had no time to make a page for Carson Cane in her notebook. Seconds later there was another knock at the door. This time, it was Roland Walker.

"You wanted to see me?" he asked, sitting down. He was smiling. Ellie did not return the smile.   50

"Was Terry a good security guard?" Ellie asked quickly.

"Sure, I guess," Roland answered. "He did a fine job."

"So it didn't bother you that he stole from your shop?"

Roland did not answer for a few seconds. He shifted in his chair. He was no longer smiling. "You've been talking to Billy," he said dryly.   55

"I have," she agreed. "He told you a month ago that Terry was the one who broke into your shop."

"He told me that he thought it was Terry. He didn't know for sure. He had no proof." Roland was starting to raise his voice.

"And what did Terry say when you asked him about it?"   60

Roland scratched behind his ear. "I didn't say anything to him about it," he said quietly.

"Excuse me?" Ellie leaned in, pretending not to hear.

"I never said anything to Terry. I never said anything to Sara, either. I don't know if he did it or not. He was married to my sister. I didn't want him to go to jail. But that is in the past. Besides, does it matter now? Terry is gone."   65

Ellie forced a laugh. "Does it matter now? Of course it matters now, Mr. Walker. You have a motive, and you have no alibi."

Roland hung a strange expression on his face. Ellie was not sure if he was angry, sad, or both. "Are we done here?" he asked.

Ellie could not think of any more questions. She was tired of sitting in interview rooms. "We   70
are done. For now." She imagined that her expression looked like Roland's—angry, sad, or both.

Roland left without another word. Ellie waited for a few seconds and left as well. She needed some fresh air, and there were some benches behind the police station. Ellie rested there for a few minutes. She called her daughter, Sofia, but the call went to voicemail. "Oh well," she whispered, closing her phone without leaving a message. She tried hard not to yawn. She was tired. She was also   75
disappointed that Roland Walker had lied to her. "Come on, Eliana," she said to herself. "Get up, keep going. There is work to do."

Wells was waiting for her back at her desk. "Don't take your coat off," Wells said, and then laughed. "Now that I think about it, do you *ever* take your coat off?"

"Where are we going?" Ellie asked.   80

Seeing that Ellie was in a bad mood, Ellie wiped off her smile. "Carson Cane called me back. He wants to meet right now. A coffee shop in Dupont Circle."

"Did he say anything else?"

"Only that he was wearing a suit and a black tie."

Ellie's blood was flowing again. She smiled at Wells. "So, he didn't confess to the murder?"   85

"Did I forget to mention that part?" Wells joked.

The coffee shop was only a five minute drive from the station. Ellie parked on a side street. It was about 3:00 p.m. and the streets were crowded. Dupont Circle was one of Washington DC's most popular shopping neighborhoods. Many tourists and locals enjoyed its bookshops, clothing stores, and restaurants. Ellie and Natalie Wells entered the loud, crowded coffee shop and started looking for the   90 man with the black tie.

He was easy to find. The tall, sandy-haired man was seated in a corner booth, playing with the handle of his mug. He watched Ellie as she and Wells approached the table.

"Mr. Cane?" Ellie asked, extending her hand.

The man did not answer, but he shook her hand and pointed to the two empty chairs across   95 from him. He was younger than Ling Cane. His skin was pale, like it never saw the sun. His thin lips and narrow nose seemed too small for his large body.

"Actually," he said slowly, waiting for both women to sit, "I am not Carson Cane. I am, however, the one who called you, Officer Wells."

Ellie and Wells quickly looked at each other. Ellie, sensing danger, put her fingers on the   100 handle of her gun. "Well then, who are you?"

"My name is Flint. I have information that can help you with your case, Detective Koo."

"How do you know my name?" Ellie asked quickly. She also looked around the coffee shop with more care.

"Don't worry," Flint said, looking at Ellie, still playing with the handle of his mug. "You and I   105 are on the same team."

"And the two men over there?" Ellie asked, nodding to her right.

"You have a good eye, detective," said Flint, smiling for the first time. "They are with me. Same team."

Ellie took another look at the men on the other side of the coffee shop—black suits, black ties,   110 serious looking.

"Do you all shop at the same store?" Wells asked. She was joking, but her voice was shaking. "What is going on here, Mr. Flint?"

"Agent Flint," he corrected her. He put his hand inside his suit pocket. Ellie tensed for a moment. Flint pulled out a badge and showed it to both women.   115

"CIA?" Ellie asked, reading the badge. The CIA, or Central Intelligence Agency, was a powerful, secretive organization within the United States government. "What's going on here?"

"You are looking for Carson Cane," Agent Flint said quietly. He put his CIA badge back into his pocket. "You called his hotel in Philadelphia. You called his employer. Why are you looking for Mr. Cane, detective?"

Ellie held the CIA agent's stare. "Why are you asking me, Agent Flint?"

Flint's fingers were back on the handle of his mug. He spun the mug in a circle. Finally he said, "Mr. Cane helps the CIA, Detective Koo. He was not involved in the Terry Sweet murder. He was with us last night."

"Carson Cane is a spy?" Wells blurted out. She immediately looked embarrassed.

Flint raised his eyebrows. "He helps the CIA. You can call him a spy if you want to."

"Agent Flint," Ellie insisted, "where was Carson Cane last night?"

"He was with us. He was not even in the country."

"Can you prove it?"

Flint's thin lips formed a smile. "I don't need to prove it, detective. I am telling you this to be nice. I am trying to help you so that you do not waste time trying to find Carson Cane. He is not your killer."

Ellie held her tongue. She thought about her options. Really, she had no options. The CIA was much more powerful than the Washington DC police force. Agent Flint did not have to answer her questions.

Ellie decided that her only choice was whether to stay or go. She stood up. "Well, thank you for your time," she said, offering her hand.

"Likewise," Flint said, standing as well.

"Oh, just one more thing," Ellie said. She did not let go of Agent Flint's hand. "Does Carson's wife, Ling, also help the CIA?"

"Does it matter?"

Ellie shrugged. "It might." She was still shaking Flint's hand.

"In that case, no. Ling Cane does not help the CIA."

"But does she know that her husband does?"

Flint's hand was starting to sweat. Ellie only smiled.

"I really must be going," he said.

"Come on, Agent Flint. Does Ling Cane know that her husband is a spy?"

"She knows," he said. Ellie let go of his hand. "She knows that Carson is not really a computer salesman."

Wells gave Flint a much shorter handshake and followed Ellie out of the coffee shop. They did   150
not speak until they reached the car.

"The CIA? I can't believe it!" Wells exclaimed. "Do you believe what he said about Carson
Cane?"

"I don't know what to believe," Ellie replied. She needed some time to think, so she dropped
Wells back at the station and continued driving to Eagle Eye Pawn Shop.   155

> Earlier in this chapter, Ellie drew pictures with rectangles and circles to help her organize the facts of the case.
> She did not have time to make a page for Carson Cane. Help her to make one here.

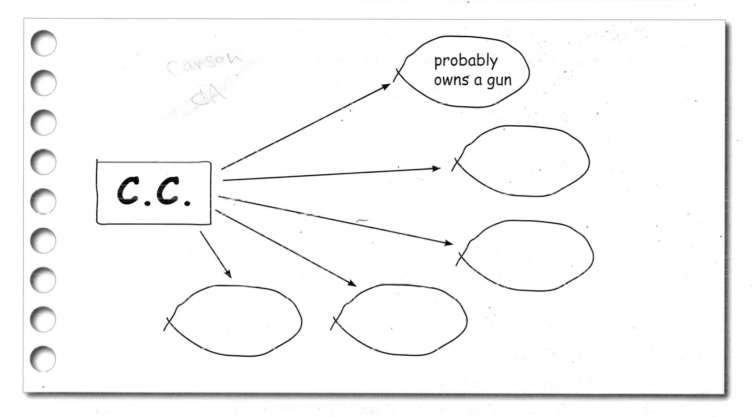

Eagle Eye Pawn Shop was finally empty. She showed her badge to an officer and slipped inside.
In the back, the chalk outline of Sweet's body still guarded the vault. Remembering the fragments of
pine, she looked around for broken furniture. She found none. Tired, she sat down on a stool inside
the vault. Everything was still inside. Again she had the feeling that she was very close to a clue, that
there was something important that she was not seeing yet.   160

She looked back at the outline of Sweet's body. Again she wondered why his arms were open
so wide. Usually when someone is shot in the chest, they cover their wounds. But not Terry Sweet. She
thought of the objects in his pockets. His gun, still in its holster. His wallet, full of money. The paper
with the vault's combination, 16-33-28. His keychain, and Billy's key to the store. The key that Sweet
stole. *Well*, Ellie thought, *Sweet probably wasn't going to steal the key. He switched it with one of his own   165
keys, and was probably going to put Billy's key back...*

And then she had it. She had her clue. She knew. Ellie closed her eyes and thought it over again. Her idea made sense. There was an object in the vault that she needed to see. After she studied it, she had to laugh.

"It was so obvious," she laughed to herself. "I can't believe that I didn't notice it earlier." 170

Ellie stepped out of the vault and took out her cell phone. She looked at the outline of Sweet's body while waiting for Wells to answer the phone.

Shaking her head, Ellie said to the outline, "You weren't stealing anything from the vault. It's just like the key. You were making a switch."

Wells finally answered the phone. 175

"Officer Wells, do you still have the videotape that we found in Terry Sweet's house?"

"Yes, ma'am, I do."

Ellie told Wells what she was looking for. She waited until Wells could rewind and watch the tape.

"I see Leo Mench opening the vault," Wells reported. 180

"Can you see inside the vault?"

"Hold on. Yes, now I can."

Then Ellie asked Wells a very simple question:

" ___	___	___	___	___	___	___	___	___	___	___	___	___
8	6	12	2	11	20	7	18	4	10	17	15	1

___	___	___	___	___	___	___	___	___	___	___	___
18	12	4	16	10	5	11	1	15	6	20	13 8 15

___	___	___	___	___	___	___	___	___	___	___	___	?"
16	6	18	5	14	3	16	1	11	20	19 11 4	20 13 4 20 9	

"Hold on," Wells said. Ellie could hear her counting. Finally Wells said, "Five. I count five."

Ellie took a deep breath and said, "I know who killed Terry Sweet." 185

END OF CHAPTER 5 END OF CHAPTER 5 END OF CHAPTER 5

CHAPTER 5: PUZZLE

Instructions:

To discover what Ellie asked, answer the following vocabulary and comprehension questions. After you have answered all of the questions, use the letters of the correct responses and the circled letters to solve the puzzle on page 138.

A. Vocabulary Questions

1) "Billy shrugged his shoulders and yawned. He seemed comfortable for the first time." (Line 12) All of these statements about <u>yawning</u> are true *except*:
   q) that you must open your mouth to yawn
   r) that you must close your eyes when you yawn
   s) that yawning is often a sign that you are tired
   t) that yawning is like taking a big breath of air

2) "He told me not to worry about it. He said that he would handle it." (Line 20) Which definition of <u>handle</u> is correct in this sentence?
   m) to take care of something
   n) to sell or trade something
   o) to hold something with your hands
   p) to operate a machine

3) "So it didn't bother you that he stole from your shop?" (Line 53) If something <u>bothers</u> you, then you:
   r) are surprised by it
   s) don't know anything about it
   t) agree with it
   u) don't like it

4) "Roland did not answer for a few seconds. He shifted in his chair." (Line 54) To <u>shift</u> means to:
   g) talk quietly, or mumble, to yourself
   h) make a loud noise
   i) change the position of your body
   j) listen very carefully

5) "He [Roland] was no longer smiling. 'You've been talking to Billy,' he said dryly." (Line 55) If you say something <u>dryly</u>, then you say it:
   r) with anger
   s) without emotion
   t) very quickly
   u) so that no one else can hear

6) "The tall, sandy-haired man was seated in a corner booth, playing with the handle of his mug." (Line 93) What drink is usually served in a <u>mug</u>?
   l) soda
   m) water
   n) wine
   o) coffee

7) "'Carson Cane is a spy?' Wells blurted out." (Line 125) What is the job of a <u>spy</u>?
   x) to fight in a war
   y) to discover information that is secret
   z) to make agreements between countries
   a) to help a country show a good image

8) "'Carson Cane is a spy?' Wells blurted out." (Line 125)

   If you <u>blurt something out</u>, then you say it quickly without

   T (h) _ i _ _n_ _k_ _i_ _n_ _g_ first.

9) "'Agent Flint,' Ellie insisted, 'where was Carson Cane last night?'" (Line 127) Which word or phrase is the *opposite* of <u>insist</u>?
   g) give up
   h) continue
   i) shout
   j) tell the truth

10) "Ellie held her tongue. She thought about her options." (Line 133)

   If you <u>hold your tongue</u>, then you do not

   _t_ _a_ (l) _k_ .

11) "Ellie shrugged. 'It might.'" (Line 142) When you <u>shrug</u>, your ___ move ___.
   y) ears; back and forth
   z) eyes; very quickly
   (a) shoulders; up and down
   b) hands; in circles

Why does a person shrug?

_____

12) "She [Ellie] showed her badge to an officer and slipped inside." (Line 156) Which definition of <u>slip</u> is correct in this sentence?
   t) fall down
   u) give something to somebody quickly
   v) make a mistake
   (w) move quietly

B. Comprehension Questions

13) Wells discovered that Carson Cane never arrived

   at his ___ ___ (+) ___ ___ .

14) Roland gives all of the following reasons for not telling anyone about Terry possibly robbing his shop *except*:
   c) that Terry told Roland that he was innocent
   d) that there was no proof that Terry was guilty
   e) that he did not want Terry to go to jail
   f) that Terry was married to Roland's sister

15) We can guess that Ellie was upset about her confrontation with ___ in this chapter.
   b) Terry Sweet
   c) Billy Stemper
   d) Carson Cane
   (e) Roland Walker

16) Why does Agent Flint tell Ellie that she has a "good eye"?
   q) Ellie understands that Agent Flint has more power than she does.
   (r) Ellie notices the two other agents in the coffee shop.
   s) Ellie realizes that Agent Flint is not really Carson Cane.
   t) Ellie has beautiful eyes.

17) How does Ellie get information from Agent Flint about Ling Cane?
   t) She promises not to tell anyone that Carson Cane works for the CIA.
   u) She offers to share information about the case with him.
   (v) She makes him feel uncomfortable with her handshake.
   w) She shows him her gun.

18) Why does Agent Flint meet with Ellie?
   p) to warn her that she is in danger
   q) to ask her what she knows about Terry Sweet's murder
   r) to give her the gun that was used to kill Terry Sweet
   (s) to tell her that Carson Cane is innocent of the crime

19) Ellie asks Wells to watch the

   ___ ___ ___ ___ ___ ___ (___) ___

   one more time.

20) Ellie is thinking about the ___ that Terry switched with Billy when she realizes something important about the case.
   m) letter
   n) key
   o) gun
   p) suitcase

Now, go back to page 138 and fill in the puzzle answers to find out what Ellie asked.

A. Police Briefing

Get into small groups and select a chief detective. The chief detective will lead group discussions, and make sure all members are participating.

1. Check your Chapter 5 puzzle answers with your group.

2. Discuss the evidence and complete the box below.

> Ellie is sure that she has found the killer. Something about the painting in the vault seems to be important. What could it be? Discuss with your group.

_____

_____

_____

_____

B. **Listen to the CD**

You will hear a voicemail message from Dwayne Potts, the assistant manager at a hotel. He has information about Ling Cane's husband, Carson Cane. After you listen, answer the questions.

1. Is Mr. Potts an experienced assistant manager? Explain.

_____

2. Who is Ms. Robinson, and why does Mr. Potts mention her when he is talking about Carson Cane's reservation?

_____

3. Do you think that Mr. Potts knows that Carson Cane is a spy? Why or why not? Discuss.

C. Think Ahead

Ellie is attracted to Roland Walker. Should she follow her feelings? Or are there other things she should think about? Discuss with your group.

D. Quiz

Complete the quiz. You may use your Detective's Notebook, but close this book.

Chapter 6 : Pre-reading

Previously in *Whodunit... The Meeting*

The following panels show three important events from Chapter 5. Order and caption each panel.

Chapter 6 : Guilty, Guilty, Guilty

In this chapter, Ellie finally puts the pieces of the puzzle together and confronts Terry Sweet's killer. In the process, she solves more than one mystery.

• **Answer these pre-reading questions alone or with a partner. If you don't know the answer, guess.**

1. The big question is: Why did Ellie ask Wells about the swirls in Chapter 5? What do you think?

_____

2. Leo Mench's purple suitcase is important in this chapter. Can you guess why?

_____

3. Who do you think is guilty of the murder? What was his or her motive?

_____

Chapter 6

Crime Talk: badge, blackmail, CIA, confess, evidence, frame, handcuffs, robbery, suspect, under arrest, warrant, weapons

Guilty, Guilty, Guilty

Ellie had a suspect in mind, but she needed evidence. After a few phone calls, she thought that   1
she knew where to find that evidence. Now she had nothing to do but wait.

She sat on a bench in front of U Street Camera. Roland Walker was not inside. The store
was dark. The Cane Gallery was just as dark and empty. It was almost 6:00 p.m. and the streets were
crowded. Many pedestrians stopped in front of Eagle Eye Pawn Shop. There were no more officers on   5
duty, but the yellow police tape held the pedestrians back.

Ellie made a quick call to her neighbor—and sometime babysitter—Vi Nguyen. Sofia was
there, doing her homework.

"Don't worry about me, mom," Sofia said sweetly. "Just go get the bad guy."

Ellie smiled at that. She hoped to be home soon, with the bad "guy" under arrest.   10

It got dark so early in the winter. The sun was almost down already. To the west, the sky over
U Street still held some blue, but to the east it was almost black. Ellie remembered looking down the
same street that morning, watching the sun come up. "What a long day," she said to herself. She took
a deep breath and searched for warmth inside her coat. Her breath swirled in front of her. She smiled.
More swirls. When she saw Yokota and Wells step out of a police car, she stood up to greet them.   15
Yokota was waving a piece of paper in his hand.

"Is that the warrant?" Ellie asked.

Yokota nodded and handed it over. "The judge signed it ten minutes ago."

The warrant gave the police permission to enter a building. "Then let's go in," Ellie said.

"Wait," Wells said quickly. "Look."   20

Ellie followed Wells' gaze. A light was on inside the Cane Gallery. Then it clicked off.

"Hurry," Ellie said, already running to the front door.

"I'll go to the back door," Yokota said.

Ellie reached the door first. She saw a shadow moving inside. "Police!" she called out, banging on the glass. "We have a warrant. Turn the lights on and show me your hands!" Her right hand was   25
holding her gun.

For a moment, nothing happened. Wells was at her side now, gun also drawn. Then the lights came on. For a second it was too bright to see. Then both women relaxed when they saw Ling Cane, her hands high above her head.

Ling opened the first door and stepped into the small entrance where Terry Sweet kept his desk   30
and chair. There was still one door between Ellie and Ling.

"What do you want?" Ling asked. She was dressed all in black now, not red. Her long, black hair covered much of her face.

"We have a warrant to search your gallery, Mrs. Cane," Ellie said in her most unfriendly voice.
"You can open the door, or I can break the glass."   35

Wells charged through the door as soon as Ling opened it. Within seconds, Ling was pinned against the wall and Ellie was searching her for weapons. "She's clean," Ellie said, and Wells relaxed her hold. Yokota appeared in the back of the gallery. He stopped running when he saw that Ellie and Wells had the situation under control.

Wells pulled Ling into the main gallery. Ellie noticed that several pedestrians were watching   40
them through the windows. She flashed her police badge, locked the door, and pulled the curtains shut. When she entered the gallery, Ling and the officers were waiting in silence.

Ellie let the silence grow for a few more seconds. Then she said, "Mrs. Cane, I have arrested a lot of suspects in my life. The innocent ones are usually surprised and ask a lot of questions. The guilty ones do not say very much. Mrs. Cane, you are not saying very much."   45

"What do you want me to say?" Ling asked. She looked tired and broken. *She is caught and she knows it*, Ellie thought.

"To start with, you can tell me why you killed Terry Sweet. I have a good idea already, but maybe you can explain it all to me."

Ling finally came to life. She tossed back her hair and said, "If you are so smart, then why don't 50
you explain it to me?" There was a chair against the wall. Ling sat in it; arms crossed, she stared at
Ellie.

"I can try," Ellie said, digging her hands deep into her coat pockets. Yokota and Wells backed
away. "First of all, I think that you probably lied about having an affair with Terry. I suspect that your
relationship was all business. I think that Terry was working for you." 55

"Of course he was working for me," Ling said, laughing. "He was my security guard."

"That's not what I mean, Mrs. Cane. Terry was doing a special job for you. He videotaped Leo
Mench opening the Eagle Eye vault. He stole Billy Stemper's key. He did these things for you, so that
you could get inside Leo Mench's vault."

"And what did I want to steal from the vault?" Ling asked, trying to stay cool. 60

Now it was Ellie's turn to laugh. "That's the funny thing," she said. "You didn't want to steal
anything. In fact, you put a very valuable painting inside the vault." Ling was not smiling now.

"It's your brother's fault," Ellie continued. "Your brother runs another art gallery in Singapore.
He sells some Ross Curran paintings there. In fact, Leo Mench bought a painting when he was there
because it was so cheap." Ellie paused, giving Ling a chance to say something. Ling chose to stay quiet. 65

"This is what I imagine," Ellie continued. "Leo Mench came back from Singapore. He wanted
to show you his new Ross Curran painting. You certainly recognized the painting right away. The
gray background with spots. The snake-like silver swirls." Ellie glanced at the painting to Ling's right.
"Much nicer than The Dinner Party, in my opinion. But there was a problem. That painting was not in
Singapore. It was here, in Washington, in your vault. You looked more closely. Then you noticed, like I 70
finally noticed. Leo Mench's painting was such a bad fake that it did not even have the correct number
of swirls."

Ellie heard Officer Wells whisper, "Ah, I see."

"The painting that is in Mr. Mench's vault right now has six silver swirls in the sky. That is
the real painting. That is the painting that you and Terry put inside the vault last night. However, the 75
painting in our videotape has only five swirls. Officer Wells counted them for me. I'm sure that when
we look at the two paintings more closely we'll see many other differences."

Ling was crying now. She was not sobbing, but large tears were slowly rolling down her cheeks.
Finally she whispered, "My stupid brother."

"It'll be better if you confess everything," Ellie said, pulling a packet of tissues from her pocket. 80

Ling did not take the tissues, but kept talking. "When I saw the painting, I knew that my
brother was making fakes in Singapore and selling them behind my back. I called him and told him to
stop, but it was too late. Mench had a fake painting and was going to show it to Ross Curran. He

wanted Curran to write him a personal note on the back of the painting. Ross would know that it was
a fake. He would take his paintings from my gallery and sue me for every penny I have. I would lose   85
everything. I could not let that happen."

"So you asked Terry for help," Ellie prompted.

"Not at first. First I tried to get the painting from Leo. I told him that I would reframe it.
I told him that I would show it to Ross myself. I tried everything. Leo refused. He would not take
that painting out of his vault. Stubborn old man." She spit out the last three words with anger. "So   90
I went to Terry. I knew that Terry would help me. Billy Stemper was sure that Terry was the camera
thief. I also knew that Terry was an ex-police officer who stole from crime scenes. I told him about my
problem. I paid him a thousand dollars up front. I was going to pay him ten thousand more after we
finished."

Ellie had two thoughts. The first one she stored away for later. The second one she said out   95
loud: "Now I know why you killed Terry." She imagined the scene—Terry and Ling inside Leo
Mench's pawn shop. The real painting was already inside the vault. Terry had the fake painting in his
hands. "Terry wanted more money, didn't he?" Ellie asked. "How much did he want?"

"Fifty thousand!" Ling exclaimed, throwing her hands in the air. "He told me that he would go
to the police if I didn't give him fifty thousand dollars."   100

"But there was something that Terry didn't know," Ellie said quietly. "He didn't know that you
had one of your husband's guns in your pocket."

Ling looked shocked. "You know… you know about my husband?"

Ellie nodded. "Why did you bring the gun with you last night, Mrs. Cane?"

Ling sighed. She looked tired and broken again. "I don't know. I felt better with it in my   105
pocket." She sat up suddenly. "You have to understand that I didn't want to kill Terry. He was standing
there, demanding more money. We were right in front of the store window. We didn't have a lot of
time. I pulled out the gun to scare him, but I didn't mean to shoot. The shot went right through the
wood frame of the painting. Little pieces went flying everywhere. It was terrible. He fell back, still
holding the painting. He died immediately. There was nothing I could do to help him."   110

Ling paused to collect herself. Ellie heard Wells whispering excitedly to Yokota, "That's what
the pieces of wood were. And that's why his arms were open. And why he was near the vault. And why
he didn't reach for his gun."

Ellie felt sorry for Ling Cane. Just a little. It was time to end this.

"Mrs. Cane, I called your security company about an hour ago. They have a record of every   115
time someone uses a security code to enter the gallery. They can even tell if you enter through the front
door or the back door. Not only that, but they have a record of every time you open your vault. It's a

very good security company. They were very helpful when I explained the situation." Ellie knelt down, meeting Ling eye to eye. Then she took out her notebook. "You opened the back door of the gallery this morning at 3:14. Then you opened the vault at 3:15. That was the last time the vault was opened.   120
Then you locked the gallery again at 3:17. Now here you are, Ling, dressed all in black. You thought that the police would be gone now. You thought it was safe."

"Just tell me what you want, detective," Ling exclaimed.

"I want you to open the vault," Ellie said coolly. "I can break it open if I need to."

Inside the vault, it took Ellie only a few seconds to find the fake Ross Curran painting. Five   125
black swirls, and much less beautiful than the original—just as she had noticed when she saw it in the video at the Sweet house. The top of the frame was destroyed and covered in blood. Terry Sweet's blood. With the painting she found Carson Cane's CIA-issued gun. It had a silencer on it. Now Ellie understood why no one had heard the gunshot.

Minutes later, Ling Cane was in handcuffs in the back of Yokota's police car. However, Ellie   130
could not go home yet. She had one more stop to make.

"You've arrested someone?" asked Sara Sweet. She was sitting next to Roland, holding his hand for support.

"We're close," Ellie lied. "I can't go into details now, but we do have a suspect."

Sara asked more about the suspect, but Ellie patiently refused to say more. Finally Sara gave up   135
and offered Ellie some tea.

"No, no thanks. But actually, Officer Wells needs to ask you some questions about the attic. Would you mind?"

Sara looked confused, but agreed to follow Natalie Wells upstairs. Ellie and Roland Walker were left alone.   140

They studied each other in silence. Finally he said, "Why did you really come all the way out here so late, Detective Koo?"

"Actually," Ellie quietly confessed, "I came to see you."

Roland flashed a big smile. Ellie again noticed how handsome he was.

"What can I do for you?" he asked, leaning forward.   145

Ellie's face changed very suddenly. She was no longer being playful. This was all business. "You can show me your suitcase."

"Excuse me?" Roland managed to say, leaning back again.

"Your suitcase," Ellie repeated. "The large, green suitcase." She pointed to the foot of the stairs. "It was right there when I came over this morning."   150

"Why do you want to see it?" he asked nervously.

Ellie slid a piece of paper out of her coat pocket. "I have a warrant," she explained, "but since your sister has had such a terrible day, I thought we could do this quietly."

Roland sighed but stood up. Ellie waved out the window. Seconds later, Yokota entered the house. *Better safe than sorry,* Ellie thought.

Wells was still keeping Sara busy in the attic. In the guest bedroom, Yokota put on a pair of gloves and removed the green suitcase from the closet. Roland and Ellie watched him open and inspect it. Moments later Yokota held up a long purple fiber.

"You see," Ellie explained, "Leo Mench's purple suitcase is quite old. It loses fibers every time you move it."

Roland took a step back, but did not run. Two more officers were blocking the door.

"Terry told your sister that one of his bosses was going to give him a big Christmas bonus. I thought that Terry was talking about blackmailing Leo Mench, but he was not. He was talking about something else." Ellie did not say so, but that 'something else' was Ling Cane's money.

Ellie continued: "In fact, Terry was not blackmailing Leo Mench. You were. This morning, when you heard about Terry's death, you saw your opportunity. You hid the purple suitcase inside the larger green suitcase and brought it over. You put it here in the guest bedroom before I arrived. Later, when we were in the camera shop, you told me that you were going to go to your house to get some clothes. But why did you need clothes if your suitcase was already here?"

"I want to make a deal," Roland exclaimed. "Do you want to know why I was blackmailing Leo Mench?"

Ellie was about to arrest Roland, but paused. "Go on," she said.

Roland looked around the room and said, "Billy and his friend were wrong. It wasn't Terry who stole the cameras from my shop. It was Leo Mench's son, Noah."

"What?" Ellie and Yokota said at the same time.

"Noah is a bad kid. He used to work with his father, back before Billy was there, but he was always stealing. It was Noah who broke the windows of the Cane Gallery. It was Noah who broke into my store."

"How do you know?" Ellie asked.

"One of Noah's friends goes to my church. About a month ago, the friend had a fight with Noah and decided to tell me about the robbery. He told me that Noah was still breaking into stores. I asked the friend if he could take pictures of Noah breaking into a store. I gave him my smallest camera and showed him how to hide it in his coat pocket and still take pictures. I used those pictures to blackmail Leo."

Roland put his hands together and added sweetly: "So, do we have a deal? Can you help me out?"   185
Roland flashed another big smile.

Ellie lowered her voice and said…

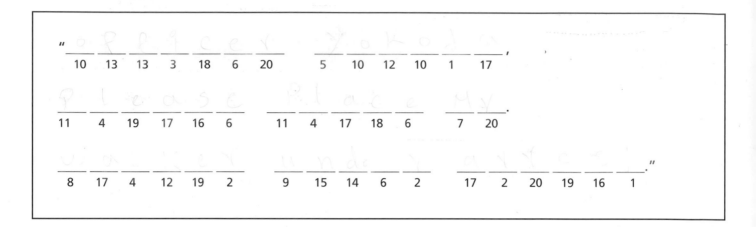

Out in the hallway, Ellie thought about the three businesses on U Street between 6th and 7th Streets. None of them would be open the next day. All three owners were guilty of something. Guilty, guilty, guilty.   190

Now it was time for Ellie to go home.

CHAPTER 6: PUZZLE

Instructions:

To discover what Ellie said, answer the following vocabulary and comprehension questions. After you have answered all of the questions, use the letters of the correct responses and the circled letters to solve the puzzle on page 150.

A. Vocabulary Questions

1) "Within seconds, Ling was pinned against the wall and Ellie was searching her for weapons." (Line 36) If you pin someone, he or she:
   - r) can't talk
   - s) can't breathe
   - (t) can't get away
   - u) can't open his or her eyes

2) "She was not sobbing, but large tears were slowly rolling down her cheeks." (Line 78)

   To sob is to ____ (___) ____ without control.

3) "When I saw the painting, I knew that my brother was making fakes in Singapore and selling them behind my back." (Line 82) The opposite of behind one's back is:
   - f) accidentally
   - g) secretly
   - h) creatively
   - i) openly

4) "He would take his paintings from my gallery and sue me for every penny I have. I would lose everything." (Line 85) Suing someone is a ___ way to get money from someone.
   - i) lucky
   - j) secret
   - k) dangerous
   - l) legal

5) "Leo refused. He would not take that painting out of his vault." (Line 89) All of these are ways to refuse a request except:
   - y) "That sounds like a good idea."
   - z) "I appreciate your offer, but I can't do it."
   - a) "No, no thank you."
   - b) "Not right now, but thanks anyway."

6) "He would not take that painting out of his vault. Stubborn old man." (Line 90)

   A stubborn person does not often

   C ___ ___ ___ ___ (___) his or her mind.

   Are you a stubborn person? Give an example of why, or why not.

   _____

7) "I pulled out the gun to scare him, but I didn't mean to shoot." (Line 108) If you did not mean to do something, then you did it:
   - l) angrily
   - m) accidentally
   - n) carefully
   - o) on purpose

8) "He died immediately. There was nothing I could do to help him." (Line 110)

   If something happens immediately, then it happens right A (___) ____ ____.

9) "It [the gun] had a silencer on it. Now Ellie understood why no one had heard the gunshot." (Line 128) What is the purpose of a silencer?
   - t) to make a gunshot straight
   - u) to make a gunshot quiet
   - v) to fix a broken gun
   - w) to make a gun difficult to find

10) "Seconds later, Yokota entered the house. Better safe than sorry, Ellie thought." (Line 155) If you agree with the expression "better safe than sorry," then you choose to be _____ even when a situation seems _____.
   - o) careful; safe
   - p) alone; dangerous
   - q) shy; comfortable
   - r) relaxed; strange

11) "Moments later Yokota held up a long purple fiber." (Line 158) All of the following contain fibers except:
  m) ropes
  n) sweaters
  o) jeans
  p) eyeglasses

12) "'I want to make a deal,' Roland exclaimed." (Line 170) If two people make a deal, then:
  i) one person gets nothing that he or she wants
  j) they give each other gifts
  k) they both get something that they want
  l) they fall in love

B. Comprehension Questions

13) Why does Ellie need to wait for Yokota and Wells at the Cane Gallery?
  f) She cannot enter the gallery without a warrant.
  g) She is afraid to enter the gallery alone.
  h) Yokota has the evidence she needs.
  i) She promised Wells that they would solve the case together.

14) Why does Ellie think that there is evidence in Ling Cane's vault?
  a) She found fingerprints on the vault.
  b) Ling's gallery is very close to the pawn shop.
  c) Terry Sweet knew the combination to Ling's vault.
  d) Ling's security company told Ellie when the vault was last opened.

15) Why did Ling go to the art gallery in this chapter?
  l) She wanted to break into Leo Mench's pawn shop.
  m) She wanted to switch a fake painting for a real painting.
  n) She wanted to remove something from her vault.
  o) She wanted to put something inside her vault.

16) Which statement can we guess is true about Ellie?
  p) She suspects that Sara Sweet is guilty of something.
  q) She does not think that Wells is ready to be a police detective.
  r) She prefers to work alone.
  s) She works late when she wants to solve a case.

17) According to Ling, why did she point her gun at Terry?
  y) He decided that it was wrong to switch the paintings.
  z) He was pointing his gun at her.
  a) He was demanding more money to finish the job.
  b) He wanted to keep the real painting for himself.

18) Ellie arrests Roland because he is guilty of

____ ____ ____ (___) ____ ____ ____ ____ ____ .

19) Ellie knew that Leo's painting was a fake because it had ____ ____ ____ (___)

____ ____ ____ ____ ____ ____ .

20) The fragments on Terry's body came from a wooden ____ (___) ____ ____ ____ .

Now, go back to page 150 and fill in the puzzle answers to find out what Ellie said.

A. Police Briefing

Get into small groups and select a chief detective. The chief detective will lead group discussions, and make sure all members are participating.

1. Check your Chapter 6 puzzle answers with your group.

2. Discuss the evidence. Use your Detective's Notebook to complete the box.

> What were the important clues that finally broke the case?

Clue	Why was it important?
The way the victim's body was found	

B. **Listen to the CD**

TRACK 12

You will hear the murderer's confession. After you listen, answer the questions.

1. What was the first question the murderer asked Terry to find out if he would help?

   ☐ Will you do something that isn't completely legal?

   ☐ Would you like to get a Christmas bonus this year?

   ☐ Do you want to earn a little extra money?

   ☐ Can you get me the code to Leo Mench's vault?

2. Why did the murderer lie to Ellie about their relationship with Terry?

   _____

3. In your opinion, what mistakes did the murderer make? Why didn't the plan work? Discuss.

C. Think Back

What did you think about this story? Would you like to read more detective stories in the future, or do you prefer a different genre? Discuss with your group.

D. Quiz

Complete the quiz. You may use your Detective's Notebook, but close this book.

Listening Scripts

The Inverted Eagle

Chapter 1: Washington DC police department investigation 09-56-79. Reed case, 9-1-1 call.

Operator:	9-1-1. What's your emergency?
Lucia:	They are dead! I think they are dead!
Operator:	Dead? Who is dead, ma'am?
Lucia:	I don't think they are breathing. Help me please.
Operator:	Ma'am, you need to calm down. Who are you talking about?
Lucia:	My boss, Mr. Evan Reed, and his wife. They're on the bed.
Operator:	I understand, ma'am. I'm sending the paramedics and the police to your home right now. We traced the phone call to 329 Birch Drive. Is that correct?
Lucia:	Yes, that's it. On the third floor. Please hurry.
Operator:	They're on their way, ma'am. Who am I speaking to?
Lucia:	Sorry?
Operator:	What's your name, ma'am?
Lucia:	Uh, Lucia, Lucia Deza.
Operator:	Lucia, I need you to check Mr. and Mrs. Reed for a pulse. Can you do that?
Lucia:	A pulse? On the neck?
Operator:	The neck or the wrist.
Lucia:	Okay, I'll try…
	Well, Mr. Reed has a pulse. But Mrs. Reed… she … I think that she…
Operator:	Take a deep breath, Lucia. Is anyone else there with you?
Lucia:	Mr. Reed's mother.
Operator:	Okay. Lucia, do you know CPR?
Lucia:	CPR?
Operator:	Yes, it's when you push someone's chest to help them breathe. Do you know how to do it?
Lucia:	I've never done it. Wait, Ms. Reed, she says she knows.
Operator:	Okay, tell her to give CPR to Mrs. Reed.
Lucia:	She's doing it.
Operator:	Great. Lucia, do Mr. and Mrs. Reed have any injuries? Is there any blood on the bed?
Lucia:	Blood? No, no blood at all. Mrs. Reed was holding a teacup and now she's all wet, but no blood.
Operator:	Is anyone else home, Lucia?
Lucia:	Home? I don't know. I don't think so. Miguel is at class. Allison is at the gym. I don't know about Kevin. I didn't see his car.
Operator:	You're doing great, Lucia. Is Ms. Reed still giving CPR?
Lucia:	Yes, but I don't think it's working. I'm going to help her.
Operator:	The paramedics will be there any second… Lucia? Lucia, are you there?

Chapter 2: Washington DC police department investigation 09-56-79. Reed case, Dr. Henry's drug analysis.

Dr. Henry: This is Dr. David Henry reporting on the… let's see here… the drug analysis in the Evan and Nancy Reed case. The date is July 24th, the time is 10:20 in the morning. I am reporting from the Wisconsin Avenue Crime Lab on a bright and sunny summer morning. Though of course I never get to go outside to see it… All right, the blood analysis shows that the drug used to knock the Reeds unconscious was a powerful, prescription-only sleeping pill called Sleepinol. I've actually used Sleepinol myself… small, round, light blue pills with a white letter 'S' printed on each pill. Very effective. Anyway, Evan Reed had about 15 milligrams of the drug in his system. The normal dosage for Sleepinol is 3 milligrams. Nancy Reed had less Sleepinol in her body, about 10 milligrams, but the effect was worse. It looks like Mrs. Reed is allergic to the active drug in Sleepinol. She never stopped breathing, but she would have in another hour or two. She is lucky that they found her when they did... I have also analyzed the tea sample and can confirm that the thief crushed the Sleepinol pills and put them in the tea. My guess is that the thief gave five or six pills to each victim. He or she was probably not trying to kill the Reeds with this amount. That's all for now.

Chapter 3: Washington DC police department investigation 09-56-79. Reed case, Officer Kazuo Yokota interviewing Paul Lipman, friend of Kevin Reed.

Yokota: This is a recording of my interview with Paul Lipman. Thank you Mr. Lipman for coming to the station.

Paul: Is it really necessary to... to record this?

Yokota: I'm afraid so, Mr. Lipman. It's official evidence, so I would recommend telling the truth.

Paul: I understand.

Yokota: Great. It says here that you are friends with Kevin Reed, that you have known him for about ten years. Is that correct?

Paul: Yes officer. It's terrible what happened to his folks.

Yokota: So you know about the crime?

Paul: Um, yeah. Kevin called me this morning.

Yokota: I see. Kevin told us that you were with him yesterday. Is that also correct?

Paul: That's right. I was with Kevin and another friend, Chip.

Yokota: At the movies?

Paul: At the... movies. That's right, the movies.

Yokota: What movie did you see?

Paul: What movie? You know, that new movie.

Yokota: No, I don't know. What's the name of the movie?

Paul: The new one with Keanu Reeves. I can't remember the name right now.

Yokota: What was it about?

Paul: Sorry?

Yokota: The movie you saw... what was it about?

Paul: Okay, there was no movie. Kevin asked me to lie about where we went yesterday. I'm really sorry. I didn't want to lie. Please don't put me in jail.

Yokota: So, where did you go?

Paul: We went to the race track. We went to Northwood Track and bet on the horses.

Yokota: Why did Kevin ask you to lie?

Paul: He lost a lot of money and didn't want anyone to know. In the ninth race he bet everything he had on a horse called Big Kevin. He thought that the horse would be lucky, since it had his name. Well, it wasn't lucky. Then he borrowed money from me and Chip, and he lost that, too.

Yokota: How much did he lose?

Paul: A lot. It was at least ten thousand dollars.

Yokota: Ten thousand dollars! Anything else I need to know, Mr. Lipman?

Paul: He was really mad at his father. He said that it was his father's fault, but I don't know what he was talking about.

Yokota: All right, Paul. I need to make a phone call. We're done. For now.

Paul: Thank goodness. Hey, I'm really sorry I lied.

Chapter 4: Washington DC police department investigation 09-56-79. Reed case, Miguel Deza suspect interview, Officer Kazuo Yokota interviewing, Part 3.

Yokota: All right, Miguel, we are recording again. Now tell me about Allison. When did you first meet?

Miguel: I met Allison when my mom started working for the Reeds. I was about thirteen years old and she was fifteen or so.

Yokota: Did you go to the same school?

Miguel: Are you kidding? The Reeds sent Kevin and Allison to private school. No, I only saw Allison at home.

Yokota: And you were friends?

Miguel: Yeah, we got along really well. When we were both in high school I helped her with her Spanish homework almost everyday. Actually, it was her idea for me to become a doctor. She told me that I was patient with

	people and good at explaining things. I never forget that.
Yokota:	So… she didn't care that you were the housekeeper's son?
Miguel:	No, Allison isn't like that.
Yokota:	So when did your relationship with Allison change?
Miguel:	At the beginning of the summer. She came back from college and everything felt different.
Yokota:	And she felt the same way?
Miguel:	I didn't know. Then, about a week after she moved back home, we both got home late one night and ate dinner together. No one else was around. She told me that I had changed a lot. She said that she used to think of me as the little boy who lived downstairs, but that I didn't seem like that little boy now. I asked her about Derrick, her fiancé.
Yokota:	And?
Miguel:	She got really upset. She said that she wasn't sure if she loved him any more. He only thought about money and didn't care about her career as a journalist. She started to cry, so I put my arm around her.
Yokota:	What a gentleman!
Miguel:	Hey, she kissed me. I told her to go to sleep and that we could talk the next day. I thought that she would forget all about the kiss and stay with Derrick. But the next day she told me that she wanted to be with me. I couldn't believe it.
Yokota:	And you didn't tell anyone about the relationship?
Miguel:	No way. We both had too much to lose. And now… now it looks like I am going to lose Allison.
Yokota:	Let's take a quick break. Then I want you to tell me all about your relationship with Evan and Nancy Reed.

Chapter 5: Washington DC police department investigation 09-56-79. Reed case, Brian Schwartz voicemail message.

Brian:	Hi, my name is Brian Schwartz. You called me earlier and left a message asking about Evan Reed. Well, I've got a lot to say about Evan Reed, and, and none of it is good. I'm very sorry that he's in the hospital, but the truth is the truth… As you know, I'm an architect with Miller and Gupta. Reed called me about a year ago and asked me to design some condos for him and his two partners. He loved my drawings and hired me to organize the entire project. The land he bought in Springfield was in a great location near the highway. I knew that he was a banker and that his wife was a lawyer, so I was sure that, uh, money wouldn't be a problem. I organized everything… I drew up all of the plans, got the contracts, hired the builders, and ordered the building materials. We started the project about eight months ago… Then the problems started. First, Reed lost his partners. I'm not sure what happened. I think that one of them lost a lot of money in a different project. Then we discovered that the land was too soft. We need to move the buildings about 100 meters over, which means that we need to change the plans and start building all over again. That costs money, but Reed hasn't paid me anything in four months. I owe money to a lot of people, and my bosses are very angry with me. They blame me for trusting Reed for so long. I could lose my job… Every time I talk to Reed, he says that everything will be better soon. He tells me that he has investors ready, or that he is going to get another loan from the bank, or that Ted Quenton is interested in the project. I asked him why he didn't ask his wife for help, but he wouldn't answer. Maybe she doesn't know about his problems. Anyway, I can't wait anymore. I realize now that he's not going to pay me unless I get an attorney… I hope this was helpful. If you need more information, please call me back at 202-555-9824. Good luck with the investigation.

Chapter 6: Washington DC police department investigation 09-56-79. Reed case, Suspect confession.

Suspect:	Are we recording? My name is ⬚⬚⬚⬚⬚⬚⬚⬚⬚. I have written this statement of confession with the help of my lawyer. I have been arrested for ⬚⬚⬚⬚⬚⬚⬚⬚ with the sleeping pill Sleepinol. I admit to this crime. I also admit to hiding ⬚⬚⬚⬚⬚⬚ in an attempt to ⬚⬚⬚⬚⬚⬚ . . . It happened like this. About two weeks ago I started to notice that ⬚⬚⬚⬚⬚⬚⬚⬚ seemed closer to each other than before. They joked together more often and always seemed to be coming and going at the same time. I decided to ⬚⬚⬚⬚⬚⬚ , to see if they were meeting outside of the house. Sure enough, I saw ⬚⬚⬚⬚⬚⬚ , and when ⬚⬚⬚⬚⬚⬚ there was no question that ⬚⬚⬚⬚⬚⬚ . I was angry and disappointed. I have known for several months that ⬚⬚⬚⬚⬚⬚ in financial ruin, although ⬚⬚⬚⬚⬚⬚⬚⬚⬚⬚⬚ . I didn't worry because I knew that

would fix everything. But then I saw ████████████████████████ . A few days later, I snuck ████████████████████████ . I knew then that their relationship was serious. The first thing I did was tell ████████████████ , but I knew that I'd have to do more… The idea of ████████████ came when I saw ████████████ standing near ████████████████ in the kitchen. I knew that ████████ would never notice a few missing pills, so I took out ten. I wasn't sure how to ████████ . Then on Sunday ████████████████ gave me the perfect opportunity. She came home late ████████████ , but I didn't hear her because I was listening to my MP3 player. Detective Koo was wrong. I was ████████████ , but I did see ████████████████████████ . I watched them ████████████████ and knew that ████████████████████████████ the combination to the safe… The next day, I ████████████████ and threw it in the garbage. I knew ████████████████ would make the police suspicious. Then, on Tuesday, I was ████████████ and asked her to go ████████████████ . When I was alone, I took the items out of the safe. I got some gloves and a screwdriver and put the items in the air vent, ████████████ , which I found ████████████ . I decided to wait only until Friday. If the perfect moment did not arrive, I would put the items back in the safe and forget about the plan. But then, on Wednesday night, ████████████████████ ████████████████████ . Only ████████████████ . When ████████████ in the shower, I ground five pills into each tea cup. Then I waited for ████████████████ , to make sure that it would work. When it did, I opened the safe and then ████████████████ . I had no idea that ████████████████████████████ . . . That's all. That's how it happened.

Death on U Street

Chapter 1: Washington DC police department investigation 09-86-22. Sweet case, 9-1-1 call.

Operator:	9-1-1. What's your emergency?
Cynthia:	I was outside that pawn shop on U Street and there was a body inside. I'm sure of it.
Operator:	All right, I understand. Which pawn shop, ma'am?
Cynthia:	The one by the camera shop.
Operator:	Which block, ma'am?
Cynthia:	Okay, hold on. I'm on 5th now and I ran about two blocks, so I guess it was the corner of U Street and 7th.
Operator:	I'm sending the police and paramedics there now. What's your name, ma'am?
Cynthia:	Cynthia, Cynthia Dewberry.
Operator:	Are you alone, Cynthia?
Cynthia:	Yes, all alone.
Operator:	Okay. Please tell me exactly what you saw.
Cynthia:	Yeah, okay. Well, I always walk by the pawn shop on the way to work and on the way home. In the back of the store there is this beautiful lamp that I've been wanting to buy. I put my hands up to the glass and looked into the store, trying to see if the lamp was still there, and that's when I saw him.
Operator:	Him?
Cynthia:	I think it was a 'him.' Looked like he had a beard. So I saw the body and I started screaming. Then I looked around and saw that there was no one else on the street, at least no one close by. I got scared. I thought that maybe the killer was still around, so I ran away.
Operator:	And this just happened?
Cynthia:	Well, actually it happened about five minutes ago. I was too scared to do anything except hide behind a tree and look to see if anyone was following me. Then I called you. Sorry I didn't call right away.
Operator:	It's all right, Cynthia. Did you notice anything else unusual at the pawn shop?
Cynthia:	No, nothing. The windows weren't broken and no lights were on.
Operator:	Your cell phone number is 202-555-7121?
Cynthia:	That's right.
Operator:	All right, Cynthia. The police will be there any second. I need you to return to the scene, to talk to the officers there. Can you do that for me?
Cynthia:	When I see the police cars I'll go back. Is that good enough?
Operator:	That's fine, Cynthia. I'll tell the officers that you'll be coming.
Cynthia:	I think I see them now. Here I go.

Chapter 2: Washington DC police department investigation 09-86-22. Sweet case, William Stemper's message left on Sara Sweet's voicemail.

Billy:	Sara, it's me, Billy. Billy Stemper. I'm outside Eagle Eye right now and I've got some news to tell you. It's not good news. It's about Terry. Goodness, I don't know how to say this. I should probably tell you face to face, but I guess it's too late for that now. Anyway, the news is that Terry is… well, he's dead, Sara. He was killed some time last night inside the pawn shop. I just talked to the police detective in charge, but they don't know anything so far… I guess that I should tell you everything that I know. At about 5 o'clock I was still in bed and I heard an ambulance siren. I jumped out of bed and stuck my neck out the window. I couldn't see much, but it looked like the ambulance was stopping right by the shop, so I ran out there. I told an officer who I was and he went to get the detective. And then I heard some woman talking to an officer. She was the one who called 9-1-1. She described the guy she saw in the shop… tall, African-American, short beard… anyway, I knew who she was talking about… Then the detective came out to see me and she asked me all kinds of questions. I'm sure she'll be coming to your house soon… I guess I'm talking too much. You must be in shock right now. If you want to call me back, my number is 202-555-0708. If there's anything you need… if you need someone to talk to, or if you want someone to help you around the house… well, I'm here if you need me. Sorry to be the one to give you this news. Well, goodbye, I guess.

Chapter 3: Washington DC police department investigation 09-86-22. Sweet case, coroner's notes.

Dr. Alvarez: The time is 8:18 a.m. on December 17th and I'm about to begin the autopsy of Terrance Sweet. This is Doctor Renzo Martinez, assisting me is Doctor Rebecca Parsons. [click] Victim was in his mid-thirties, excellent condition, weight 187 pounds. Cause of death appears to be a single gunshot to the chest. The bullet struck the victim's heart. I suspect that he died immediately. Doctor Parsons found an additional injury on the back of the head. This probably occurred when the victim fell back after being shot. [click] There are several small fragments of wood in and near the wound in the chest. I will send some samples to the crime lab, in case they don't have any. [click] The body temperature is 92 degrees Fahrenheit. Under normal conditions, body temperature drops about 1 degree per hour after death. Therefore, I estimate the time of death at approximately 3:00 a.m. [click] I have completed my analysis of the victim. He was healthy inside and out, with the exception of his liver and lungs. The state of his liver suggests that Mr. Sweet was a heavy drinker. Scarring in his lungs suggests that he was a heavy smoker. [click] I can confirm that the cause of death was the gunshot to the heart. I estimate that the shooter was about eight to ten feet away from the victim when the shot was fired. [click] The autopsy is complete and there is nothing further to report at this time. The time is 9:29. Martinez out.

Chapter 4: Washington DC police department investigation 09-86-22. Sweet case, Crime lab report on wood fragments.

Dr. Henry: Dr. David Henry here. This is my report on the small fragments of wood found on the victim in the Terrance Sweet shooting. Today is December 17th, the time 9:40 in the a.m. I am reporting from the Wisconsin Avenue Crime Lab on a wonderfully chilly morning, though of course I never get to leave my lab, not even for breakfast... Well, I can report that the wood fragments are indeed pine. At first I thought that it was a different wood, maybe oak, because of its dark color, but what I was seeing was a dark finish. In other words, this is not wood straight off of the tree, but rather from a piece of furniture or something like that... I just spoke with Dr. Martinez, who conducted the autopsy and sent me several samples from the wound. He estimates between ten and fifteen fragments on the body, most near the wound. The report from the scene of the crime states that more than thirty other fragments were found on the floor. None of the fragments are longer than one centimeter. I see two possibilities. The first is that a very small wooden object was destroyed, probably by the bullet. The second possibility is that a small piece of a larger object was hit by the bullet. In truth, there is one other possibility, that the bullet did not break the wood apart. I have examined the bullet, sent to me by Dr. Martinez, but cannot be sure. That's all for now.

Chapter 5: Washington DC police department investigation 09-86-22. Sweet case, Voicemail message from Dwayne Potts, assistant manager of Tower Hotel.

Dwayne: Hi, this is a message for Officer Natalie Wells. My name is Dwayne Potts and I'm the assistant manager at Tower Hotel in Philadelphia. The manager, Ms. Robinson, is not available, and this is only my third day as assistant manager, but I hope that I'll be able to help you. The front desk said that you called asking about a guest, Mr. Carson. No, wait. Mr. Cane, Mr. Carson Cane. Sorry about that... Anyway, I asked around and it turns out that Mr. Cane is not here at the hotel. He was supposed to arrive on Sunday and stay for four nights. His company paid for the room, so we are keeping it empty, but Mr. Cane never arrived. The computer says that the hotel manager, Ms. Robinson, handled the payment herself, and that Ms. Robinson spoke to Mr. Cane's company and told them that he wasn't here. But like I said, Ms. Robinson isn't available today... Today is Wednesday, so tonight is the last night that Mr. Cane's company paid for. If Mr. Cane shows up, or if I discover anything else, I'll be sure to call you. If you have any other questions for me, please call the Tower Hotel at 1-800-555-8134 and ask for Mr. Dwayne Potts. Or you can ask for the assistant manager. That's me.

Chapter 6: Washington DC police department investigation 09-86-22. Sweet case, Suspect confession.

Sonia: We've started recording once again. Present in the interview room are ⬛⬛⬛⬛⬛⬛⬛⬛⬛⬛ , and me, Sonia Vichi, assistant district attorney. ⬛⬛⬛⬛⬛⬛ , we've already discussed what happened in the early morning hours of Wednesday, December 17th. Now I would like to focus on your relationship with the victim, Mr. Sweet. You told Detective Koo that ⬛⬛⬛⬛⬛⬛⬛⬛ . Were you?

Suspect: No, I lied to Detective Koo about ⬛⬛⬛⬛⬛⬛ . I was sure that she had Terry's ⬛⬛⬛⬛⬛⬛ and I needed to explain why we spoke on the phone so often. There was nothing romantic about our relationship.

Sonia: You hired Mr. Sweet to help you steal the fake Ross Curran painting from Mr. Mench's vault. How did that happen?

Suspect: I knew about Terry's history with the police. Also ⬛⬛⬛⬛⬛ told me that ⬛⬛⬛⬛⬛⬛⬛ was the camera thief. So, I stayed ⬛⬛⬛⬛⬛⬛ one night about two or three weeks ago, waiting for ⬛⬛⬛ . I wasn't sure how to ⬛⬛⬛⬛⬛⬛ .

Sonia: What did you say?

Suspect: At first, I just asked him ⬛⬛⬛⬛⬛⬛⬛⬛⬛⬛⬛⬛⬛ . When he said yes, I told him ⬛⬛⬛⬛⬛⬛⬛⬛⬛ . He just laughed, and I knew ⬛⬛⬛⬛⬛⬛⬛ . I told him that the only thing I needed was ⬛⬛⬛⬛⬛⬛⬛ . It took him about a week to get it. His only other job was to ⬛⬛⬛⬛⬛⬛⬛ .

Sonia: You were going to ⬛⬛⬛⬛⬛⬛⬛⬛ ?

Suspect: That was my plan in the beginning, but then I was worried that ⬛⬛⬛⬛⬛⬛ . The paintings are quite large.

Sonia: So you asked ⬛⬛⬛⬛⬛⬛⬛⬛ ?

Suspect: It was his idea, actually. We met ⬛⬛⬛⬛⬛⬛ , on Monday morning, ⬛⬛⬛⬛⬛⬛⬛⬛ . Of course, now I know that ⬛⬛⬛⬛⬛⬛⬛⬛ when we were inside ⬛⬛⬛⬛⬛ .

Sonia: All right, ⬛⬛⬛⬛⬛⬛ . I think I'm getting a clearer picture of what happened. Let's take a break.

About the Authors

Adam Gray

Adam Gray is currently an elementary school assistant principal in Lewisville, Texas. He has taught all levels of students, from kindergarten to university, in Japan, Chile, and the United States. He holds a Bachelors degree in English from the Ohio State University, where his academic focus was on creative writing. In addition, Adam earned a Masters degree in TESOL from American University in Washington DC and another in Educational Leadership and Policy from the University of Texas at Arlington. Adam currently lives near Dallas, Texas with his wife Katty and two children, Iliana and Alexander.

Marcos Benevides

Marcos Benevides teaches English at J. F. Oberlin University in Tokyo. He holds a Masters in Education from the University of Calgary, and an Honours B.A. with a double major in literature and creative writing from Concordia University in Montreal. He is the series editor and lead writer for Choose Your Own Adventure graded readers (McGraw-Hill Education), and co-author of Widgets: A task-based course in practical English (Pearson Longman). Marcos currently lives near Tokyo with his wife, Yoko, and his young children, Kei and Maya.